The Hunter and The Trap

BOOKS BY HOWARD FAST

Torquemada	1966
The Hill	1964
Agrippa's Daughter	1964
Power	1962
April Morning	1961
The Golden River	1960
The Winston Affair	1959
Moses, Prince of Egypt	1958
Silas Timberman	1954
The Passion of Sacco and Vanzetti	1953
Spartacus	1951
The Proud and the Free	1950
My Glorious Brothers	1948
Clarkton	1947
The American	1946
Freedom Road	1944
Citizen Tom Paine	1943
The Unvanquished	1942
The Last Frontier	1941
Conceived in Liberty	1939
Place in the City	1937
The Children	1935
Strange Yesterday	1934
Two Valleys	1933

The Hunter
and
The Trap

by Howard Fast

THE DIAL PRESS, INC.
NEW YORK, 1967

For Jonathan Fast

because these are stories
that could not have been written
without the things
I learned from him.

Contents

The Hunter

1

Of course I went out to Kennedy to greet Andrew Bell. He had sent me a wire that he was coming in on the two o'clock plane, and he had also sent a wire to Jane Pierce, his public relations girl; so practically everyone in the world knew that he was coming into Kennedy at two o'clock. My going out there was of a particular nature, because sometimes I thought that I was his friend. Otherwise, why would he have sent me a wire?

I called my wife to tell her about it, and she asked me when I thought I might see her again.

"Well, tonight," I said. "You know that."

"Do I?"

"Come off it," I said. "Andy Bell is my friend. What else do you want me to do?"

"He has ten thousand friends. He has friends in Istanbul and friends in Paris and friends in Madrid and friends in London and of course in New York. I'll bet he has friends in Albuquerque."

"All right."

"All right," she repeated, and maybe she was sorry and had pushed it too far.

"It's just a funny damn thing about friends," I told her.

"I know. And you're the only real friend Andy Bell has or ever had."

"Maybe not even me," I said. "I don't know."

2

I drove out to Kennedy, and the traffic was bad, so by the time we got there, the plane had already landed. You could not miss Andrew Bell, but neither could you get very near to him, and from the number of reporters, cameras and microphones you would have guessed an ambassador, a king or a prime minister had just landed. It was that kind of a crowd. There were civilians, perhaps twenty or thirty, but for the most part the crowd was professional and the object of the crowd was news. Andy was news. He was always news.

Jane Pierce spotted me, broke out of the crowd to grab my arm, and told me to please go to him and let him see my face. She was a tall, competent blond, middle-thirties, polite, neutral and successful, and attractive in a hard way; and I was flattered that she felt that I should be with Andy. She had that manner of authority that brings importance wherever it is directed.

"He needs a hard friend," she said in my ear. "Get over to him."

If there was a distinction between hard and soft friends, there were enough in the second category. I saw Joe Jacobs, the columnist—tomorrow he would do an entire column on Andy Bell, possibly a second one the day after that; and Frank Farrell from the *News;* and Linda Hawley, the society protocol boss and party expert, who already would be contracting for Andy's delivery here and there; and pushing hard to break through, Lucy Praise, the actress, whom he had dated half a dozen times between two wives; and just behind her, Max Golden, the millionaire, who was content to be seen within shouting distance and to pick up any check that had no other takers—Andy took most of them; and Jack Minola, the punchy, ex-heavyweight fighter, who acted as a sort of Newfoundland dog to Andy when Andy was on base in New York, and who liked to think of himself as a bodyguard, self-appointed and tolerated because Andy never got over the fact that celebrities attached themselves to him—and never really comprehended what a celebrity he himself was.

But Jane got me through, and there Andy was, big and healthy and sunburned, his massive shoulders and six feet three inches of height topped by that graying mane of hair. His blue eyes crinkled with pleasure. His face was the face of a kid, and not the face of a fifty-three-year-old who had been married four times and had won the Pulitzer Prize—the face of a kid being fussed over and praised when he might have gotten a hiding instead.

The CBS man had taken the lead in the questioning, and he had just asked Andy where the safari had been this time.

"Kenya mostly. Then we flew into Somaliland."

"Did you pilot the plane?"

"Like always."

"What kind of a plane?"

"An old Piper Cub."

"And is it true you shot a lion from the plane?"

"No. Hell, no. I'm a hunter, not a circus performer."

"But you did go after lion?"

"I never hunt in Africa without thinking of lion. He's number one. I killed three lions—all male. One was a black-maned giant—the biggest lion I ever saw, possibly the biggest ever recorded there."

"Did you shoot elephant?"

"We had a kill in elephant. We had a kill in leopard too. It was a good hunt and we had a good kill."

"And are you pleased to be back in New York?"

"I am. I like New York. I like London and Paris and Madrid and Lisbon. I liked Havana once and maybe someday I'll like Havana again. And I'm glad to be in New York."

He spoke the way he wrote, and I did not know whether to laugh or to cry. He had his entourage with him, Jose Peretz and Diva. Peretz was a small, dark, tight-muscled little man with polished hair and button eyes. He carried two knives and he had been known to use them. No one knew anything about him. Some said that he had been a bad matador and others said he had been a run-of-the-mill male whore, but no one really knew anything about him except that he spoke Spanish with a Portuguese accent—when he spoke, which was not often. That was about as much as Diva spoke. She was a tall, beautiful, black-haired woman of thirty or so, and nothing at all was known about her—that is, just a little less than was known about Peretz. That was the entourage. Somehow, they made arrangements and looked after the baggage and cleared away obstacles. Now and then a pretty and young stenographer joined them: this one, that one, the girl changed. But this time there were only two.

Andy saw me. "Hey, Monte!" he boomed. "Hey, Monte, goddamn you!" And then almost without pause, he was answering a question, and he said that No, he had never killed a Rocky Mountain bighorn sheep. Then he embraced me, and I could feel the iron-hard muscles of his arms biting into me. No fat and no soft. "But I will," he added, referring to the bighorn.

Some young kid who worked for one of the TV networks asked another who I was, and the reply came, "That's Monte Case, his friend."

3

I drove him back to New York in my car, just the two of us. In the time since he had last been here, the airport had changed; the roads had changed. I think it was before

the Fair, and now the Fair was over; and I was not even
sure that the new stadium for the Mets had been here. But
he didn't notice such things, or maybe he could not admit
that anything had changed since his last visit. He closed his
eyes, stretched his long length, and said, oh, my God, he
was tired and beat up and felt every one of his fifty-three
years.

"You're young," I said inanely. I never made good or
sharp conversation with him, and I was always conscious
of the awkwardness of my comments.

"Balls, Monte. I am old as the hills and goddamn tired
of it. Why do I keep chasing my tail?"

"That's your problem, Andy."

"Another hunt. The chase and the kill. That's it.
That's really it. That's the one sweet taste. I could give up
the rest of it, the booze and the girls and all the status and
celebrity horse-shit, but not that. Where are we going?"

"Where did your luggage go?"

"The hell with the luggage. That's at the Carlyle."

"The Carlyle?"

"That's right. Jane got me the suite there. It's the
place, isn't it?"

"I suppose so. It's the place."

"I mean—since Jack's time. My God, I can't believe
he's dead. I haven't been back since then. But the hotel is
still in, isn't it?"

"Very much."

"But Jack is dead."

He had only met Kennedy once and briefly, but he was
not name-dropping or trying to impress me. All the "great"

names that flashed in and out of the press were his peers. If he was not intimate with them, it was only because time and circumstances had prevented such intimacy from developing.

"You don't want to go there?" I asked him.

"No."

"You said you were tired.'

"The hell with that! I'm always tired."

"Then where?"

"Pete's—Christ Almighty, that's still there, isn't it? Pete didn't die or anything like that, did he? Or go broke?"

"It's still there, and he didn't go broke."

"Monte, let me tell you one thing—one small, crowded fact of life. Suppose I needed twenty grand. Now. This damn bloody minute. No collateral—nothing except my marker. Where would I go?"

"Make it a smaller price and come to me."

"Balls. You know goddamn well that there's only one person in the world I can go to. There's only one person in the world that will write me a check for twenty grand and never ask why or how."

"Pete?"

"That's right."

"Did you ever try it?"

"You're a cynical bastard, Monte."

"Good, we'll go to Pete's."

"You don't mind?" he asked, concerned suddenly that he might have hurt my feelings.

"Mind? My word, Andy, this is your day, your place, and it seems to me that it is maybe your city too."

4

The doorman at Pete's had only been there a year and a half or so, and he didn't recognize Andy. Afterwards, he was filled with remorse; he had the attitude of a man who wants nothing so much as to throw himself under a truck, and he pleaded for Andy's forgiveness. "You got to understand, Mr. Bell, that I'm new here. That's no excuse. But that's the way it is, that's the way the cookie crumbles, that's the way it is." Andy gave him five dollars, and the doorman swore up and down that he would never forget him again, and I suppose he didn't.

But if his welcome from the doorman was less than effusive, Pete made up for it, engulfing Andy in his three hundred pounds of fat and soft muscle and kissing him. Pete was the one man in town who could kiss another man and get away with it. They embraced and hugged each other, and then Pete yelled to the bartender:

"Mike, get the hell down to the cellar and bring up that keg of black rum that has Mr. Bell's name on it. Do it yourself. I don't want any lousy, grimy busboy hands touching that keg of rum."

"You son of a bitch," Andy said, and grinned. "You kept that keg."

"They can take away my place. Not that keg."

"You fat bastard, I love you," Andy said.

"Ha! The only thing you love, Andy, are those guns

of yours, which my friend Doc Schwartz holds are phallic symbols."

"Where is he? I'll put something up his ass for him to think about. Phallic symbols, huh? You've become goddamn classy for a saloon keeper."

"And how do you like this new saloon of mine—about two million dollars worth of it visible from where you stand?"

At this time of the afternoon—it was just past four o'clock now—the restaurant at Pete's place was practically empty, but there were a dozen or so people at the bar and the serious drinkers were beginning to drift in. There were two men from the Associated Press who recognized Andy and gathered around. Bernie Watts, the press agent, was drinking in a dark corner with Norma Smith, the red-headed belly dancer, who was just one inch under six feet tall and was making a sensation doing what she did best, which was belly dancing. She led him over, and Watts apologized decently for the intrusion.

"I got this broad with me and she says she'll take me apart if she doesn't meet you, Mr. Bell, and she's big enough to do it. The only claim I got on you is that Jane Pierce and I once shared an office."

Andy had an eight-ounce glass of black rum in his hand. He shook hands with Watts and grinned with pleasure at the redhead.

"My name's Norma," the redhead said. "You're my hero. Ian Fleming was my hero for a while but he's a lousy writer. You're the best writer in the world."

"God bless you! You ever tasted black rum?"

"No," the redhead said, licking her lips. "You pour it and I'll taste it. I don't mean that Ian Fleming couldn't tell a story. He's got something you can't knock, but no class. I mean he's gauche. You know what I mean?"

"I know one thing," Andy said. "You and me, we're going to talk about literature—right?"

Lieutenant O'Brian, who was the head of the detective squad at the local precinct, came in then, and he was introduced, and then two Hollywood male stars and their director turned up, and then a photographer who climbed onto the bar to get a few pictures. The crowd got thicker, but Norma Smith, the big belly dancer, held her place. Andy was telling Pete about the big black-maned lion, and the hubbub died down, because when Andy told a story that way, straight and clean and simple, you didn't compete or interrupt. He had laid down the background with a few plain strokes. He had been alone at the time, quite deliberately. He had wanted to do it alone. He was in a big meadow, much of it covered with waist-high grass, with here and there an open spot. He had watched the motion of the grass defining the lion's path. It was late afternoon, and the lion had not yet made its kill; and then the lion came out of the grass and the beast stood there facing Andy.

"I was in no danger from the lion," Andy said. "There are very few animals that will go for man unprovoked. A man-eating lion has the habit, but he's old and cantankerous and incapable of running down game. This lion was young and vigorous. He was about thirty yards from me, and he regarded me with small interest and less concern, and I knew that in a moment he would step back into the grass and disappear. That was when I decided to make the kill, and everything I thought about I had to think through in a fraction of a second."

He tasted his rum and then explained that the lion had been in the wrong position.

"Head on—and all I could see was his face and that great mane and his front legs. Maybe a slice of shoulder, but that kind of shot is no good. The best shot is from a parallel position, with the lion a bit ahead of you. Then you can reach the heart, and then you have time for a second shot—or your bearer has. I was alone. Only one shot and that one had to be in the brain—through the eye or the skull, and the skull can be bad. I was scared as hell. If the first shot did not kill immediately, then even a mortal wound wouldn't save my life. The lion would come in like an express train—well, I did it. It was a good kill."

"Son of a bitch," Pete said.

"You're too much," the belly dancer said. The crowd got bigger, and I recalled that it was like the old days in Pete's old place.

5

By six o'clock, Andy had put down over a pint of black rum, and he decided to throw a party at the suite at the Carlyle. I had no opinions on this subject, because I knew Andy a little. He had probably begun to drink when he boarded the plane in Africa; his capacity was enormous and his body's ability to deal with alcohol was little short of miraculous; and by now, underneath his controlled exterior, there was something wild and irresistible.

"All of you," he said, including a crowd of about twenty people clustered around us and the belly dancer. "And I want the mayor," he said to me. "I want the mayor and the mayor's wife and the governor and I want Monsignor Sheen—"

"You're out of your mind. And you're behind times. I think he's a bishop now, and he sure as hell doesn't go to parties."

"Maybe he would," Lieutenant O'Brian put in. "You don't know, Monte. You're not even a Catholic."

"And this is not even a religious matter, you will forgive me."

"And who the hell are you to say what is a religious matter?"

"Oh, wait one damn cotton-picking minute," Andy said. "You know, I met him once maybe fifteen years ago, but we were like brothers. There was good blood between us. We knew each other. We broke bread and we drank wine. He said to me, 'Andy, if you need me, call me and I'll come.'" He turned to Pete. "Look, Pete—am I stepping on anyone's toes? A man's religion is a piece of his gut. I don't have that gut. I'm one-quarter Presbyterian, one-quarter Methodist, one-quarter Episcopalian and I think one-quarter Jewish and one-quarter Mormon—"

"That's five quarters," someone snorted.

"So it's five quarters," Pete said. "And if he isn't entitled to five quarters, who the hell is? No, you're not out of line, Andy. You were never out of line."

"You're too much," the belly dancer said. "I'm a Catholic. I'm a rotten Catholic, but I am a Catholic and you're not stepping on anyone's toes."

"And I want Marc Connolly and Bette Davis there, and Eva Gabor and what's-his-name, that marvelous kid who conducts the Philharmonic?"

"Bernstein, and he's not a kid any more."

"Well, I want him to come with his wife and all his friends—"

"Andy, people like that have unlisted numbers and I don't have them."

"Pete has them. Pete has the phone number of everyone on earth who matters. Even what's-his-name in the Soviet Union. You got a number for the Kremlin, Pete?"

"I got," Pete grinned, and everyone else was grinning now because they knew that the party was in the making, and that it would be a great, fabulous party that the town would remember and talk about for years to come.

"And I want the mayor and his wife."

"Andy, it's not like old times. This is a different kind of a mayor, and he's a Republican—"

"I don't care if he's a Single-Taxer," Andy said. "Invite him. All he can do is say no." And then, to show that even if he had been away, he was as cool as any of the snotty young kids around town, Andy said to O'Brian, "Who's the lieutenant of the Nineteenth Squad? Is it still Rothschild?"

"It is."

"And how are his ulcers?"

"Rotten."

"Will you call him, lieutenant, and tell him that we will be having a drink or two with friends at the Carlyle, and that Andy Bell begs him to exhibit the quality of mercy if there is a complaint?"

Pete brought me the phone then, and I got City Hall. Everyone lapsed into a careful silence as I worked my way up to the mayor; and finally I got him and told him that Andy Bell was in town. Which he knew. And then I told him that Andy was giving a party at the Carlyle tonight and it was short notice, but would he come and bring his wife?

"I'd be delighted to come," he said. "I can't promise because it is short notice—but I'll try."

Andy and Pete hugged each other.

6

There are all kinds of parties around town. There are wild parties and lush parties, and sometimes people plan all year for a party they are going to give, and with some of the rich ones I know, a party is to be put together only by a professional party manager, like the late Elsa Maxwell. There are other parties that bear the stamp of a personality, and when Andy Bell threw a party, it grew around him, like a vine around a tree. There are parties where the host sets out to corner a few personalities and to build a certain amount of status; but if people in New York were in and important, it was up to them to know that Andy Bell was giving a party and to turn up there. It was a good thing that the suite Jane Pierce had rented at the Carlyle was a big one, because most of them turned up there.

Jane was waiting for us at the Carlyle, and she said to me, "I heard that Andy was giving a party. Was that your idea, Monte?"

"My idea? Anyway, how did you hear?"

"Because the President's kid telephoned from Texas. She wants to come, I told her to come. The hell with it. I'm going to tell the hotel to set up a bar and a table with sandwiches and junk. You know what this will cost Andy? At least two grand. And he's damn near broke."

"Why don't we get that Max what's-his-name to pick up the tab?"

"Because Andy would blow his stack."

"How can he be broke? I heard that *Life* is paying fifty thousand dollars for the story of how he shot that lion."

"He spent the fifty grand before he ever hit Africa. Take my word for it."

Andy had gone on into the suite, and now we followed him inside. Jose Peretz was explaining how he had unpacked. He had put the guns into a bedroom closet. Diva was in one corner of the big couch in the living room. She watched us silently. It was funny how no one ever asked Andy about her, who she was or what she was to any of them. Maybe she was Jose's girl, although I was inclined to think that Jose was some kind of faggot, not the ordinary kind but something esoteric; and since Diva had that lean, dry, meticulous look of a certain type of dyke about her, perhaps they matched. But no one asked about Diva, not even myself. In a way, Andy was very fond of Jane Pierce; he would embrace her and kiss her in front of Diva, and there was no reaction in the dark-haired woman that I could see. But then there was no reaction on her part to any of the play between Andy and other women—maybe because she knew that it never went beyond the opening of the game.

Andy wondered about the guns, and whether there were any new laws to make things difficult.

"You don't have any pistols?" I asked him.

"Just an old Santé automatic that I use for target practice."

"Well, don't take it out on the street, and I'll call my lawyer later and see if you need any kind of a license or whether you check it in downtown or what. I suppose the rest are rifles and shotguns?"

"That's right."

"I don't think it makes any difference, as long as you keep them here."

The big red-headed belly dancer came in then. She had changed clothes, from a daytime dress to a long, shimmery gown, and she told Andy that while it was a little early for the party to start, she was hungry, and she did not want to make a date with anyone else because she was going to lap on his ass like a hound dog all night.

"Don't you ever eat alone?" Jane asked her nastily.

"Honey, take a second look at me. Do you think I have to?"

The hotel waiters began to move in and set up, and

I went into Andy's bedroom to call my wife. Andy came in while I was waiting for my number, and then Jose came in with Andy's tuxedo.

"I had it pressed," Jose said.

He helped Andy dress. Liz, my wife, informed me that she had heard about the party.

"How could you hear?"

"The six o'clock news. Evidently, Grand Duke Alexis is flying in from Paris as some sort of publicity stunt. He expects to make the party. Am I invited?"

"You know you are."

"Not that earnestly, but it's nice to hear it from God's right-hand man."

"Will you come?"

"I wouldn't miss it for the world—if I can fight my way in. What do you expect, a thousand people?"

When I put down the phone, I told Andy about the Grand Duke Alexis.

"Who the hell is the Grand Duke Alexis?"

"Don't you remember? He used to have a restaurant in Beverly Hills. Now he has a place on the Left Bank."

"Did I ever eat there, Monte?"

"I guess you must have, because he's flying in tonight. That's a big tab for a party. You should be flattered. Look, do you want me to go home and change?"

"What for?"

"I don't know what for. I just don't want to drag the affair down. Look, Andy, are you short of cash?"

"What?" He was provoked now. I had hit a soft spot. "What in hell ever gave you that notion?"

"All I am thinking about is this damn party. It's going to take a bundle to pay for it."

"Are you serious, Monte? You're like the oldest friend I got. Otherwise, I could get real nasty."

I let the subject drop, and Andy and I went into the living room. Two tall, distinguished, white-haired Italians greeted him with pleasure. Afterwards, I learned that they were two of the top wheels in the Mafia; Andy had met them some years before when they had helped him to arrange a wolf hunt in Sicily.

The party had started early, and now, long before post time, there were already two dozen people in the room. The buffet table had been set up, and Norma Smith, the redhead, was stuffing herself with good, nourishing food, namely toast and imported caviar.

Jane Pierce whispered to her, icily, "That, darling, is thirty-six dollars a pound."

"Then it's hardly the best, is it?" the belly dancer replied.

Max Golden arrived, with two small, blond go-go girls, one hanging on to each of his arms. Their party dresses were six inches above the knee. "They're a present to you," Max said to Andy.

"What are their names?"

"Damned if I know."

Then Max saw Norma Smith, and he dropped the little go-go girls and made a beeline for the big redhead. The two kids gravitated to Jose—they thought he was "darling"; and I steered Andy over to meet the senator. You couldn't have a party like this without the senator's wife, and she had to have him with her as a door opener. The senator read books and he was really excited to meet Andy, but when he tried to talk about African politics, Andy broke away.

"He won't talk politics," I explained to the senator. "That's because he won't think politics."

"Years ago—"

"Well, that was all years ago. Things have changed."

The ambassador to the U.N. came in then, and the senator had someone to talk politics to. The management had finally produced a record player, and I had them put it out on the terrace. It was getting hot in the living room anyway, so we folded back the big double doors to the terrace and eased the increasing congestion in the living room. Jock Lewis, the radio disk jockey, was persuaded to run the phonograph, and Jose tried to teach the go-go girls some flamenco steps to the beat of rock and roll. Then I saw my wife, Liz, and I had to push people aside to reach her. She was with two pugs, one an ex-lightweight and the other an ex-heavyweight, both of them Negroes, and she yelled across to me:

"I brought some quality to your crumby party."

She was lit already. The Negro pugs embraced Andy and Jacky Minola, and they formed a little circle to talk about the fight game. The circle grew bigger.

Jane Pierce pulled me aside and demanded, "Monte— what about this? What do we do?"

"What about what?"

"This crazy party. There are already ninety-one here by head count, and look at the doorway."

It was something to think about. They were coming through the door now in almost a steady stream. I recognized two movie stars, a member of "What's My Line?" and the new parks commissioner. The quality was good.

"It's quite a party."

"If you look on it as a competition, I suppose so. I just hate to think of what the price per minute is at this moment. I didn't have time to go out and shop for bulk liquor or anything like that. It's all hotel rates, and have you ever looked at the catering sheet of this hotel?"

"No."

"You should. And where do we put them?"

"When it banks up solid, they can't get in. That's all."

"That's all?"

"Look, Jane, you can't do anything and I can't do anything. That's the way it is. Let it run its course."

"The thing that puzzles me," Jane said, "is this. A few hours ago, Andy decided to have a party. Now everyone in the world knows about it. How does that happen?"

"Word of mouth."

"You're a help."

"Well, what do you want me to do?"

"Drop dead," she said pleasantly. "When I think of something else, I'll tell you."

7

I slipped into Jose's room a little later to see whether I could make a telephone call to the manager and maybe find an adjoining suite to open up, or even a room, or maybe let the overflow into the grand ballroom or something like that; and there was Diva, sprawled on the bed and staring at me.

"Can I use the phone?" I wanted to know.

She nodded silently, and I discovered that the manager was gone for the day and the assistant manager was somewhere in the hotel—probably at the party.

"Hell with them," Diva said. I couldn't remember when I had heard her say anything else. "Let them crawl all over each other. What do you care?"

I was sitting on the edge of the bed, a few inches from where she lay sprawled out. She reached out an arm and drew me down to her, and I let myself be drawn; and then I kissed her, a wide, hot kiss, with her tongue darting in and out of my mouth like a little snake.

After that, I pulled up and away from her and said, "Whatever you want, Diva, I probably want double, but it's like trying to do it in Grand Central Station. Also, my wife is out there, and she sort of hates me and she'd love an excuse to cut my heart out."

"You afraid of her?"

I nodded. "Also, I always figured you were Andy's girl."

"Like hell you did. You are like a stinking little open book, Monte, and I read you good. You always figured me for a dyke, and you figured Jose and me, we diddled each other. Balls. I work for Andy; I'm not his girl, and I don't screw Jose backwards either. As for you, just go to hell."

"I'll see you later," I said, and then I went back to the party, leaving the door to the bedroom open, hoping that it might take some pressure off the living room. The living room was packed almost solid, but if you moved slowly and had some patience, you could penetrate. I got caught in a cluster of black men with fezzes and sweeping gowns, and then I saw Andy, who was trying to talk to them in Senegalese or Somali or Bantu or something like that; and he saw me and grinned and boomed:

"What a party, Monte! What a goddamn true, beautiful party!"

I grinned foolishly, and pushed on to Jane Pierce, who was out on the terrace, talking to a thin, worried-looking man in dinner clothes.

"I tried," I said. "The manager went home. The assistant manager is lost or something."

"This is the assistant manager, Monte," she replied. "This is Mr. Bell's friend, Monte Case."

"Well, are you responsible, Mr. Case?"

"Andrew Bell is a very responsible man."

"I know that. How does one find him?"

"He's right there in that group of Africans," I said.

"There are a great many people here," Jane said, smiling her best smile at him, "but I think it's a very genteel lot, don't you? We have two of the highest dignitaries in the local diocese—I can't remember their names but they are very estimable churchmen. That tall African—you can see his fez over the crowd—is the Prime Minister of Nigeria or Ghana or the Congo. Well, it's that sort of party—"

"Of course, of course. It's just a question of suffocation, simple suffocation. But if you keep the doors to the terrace open—"

"I wouldn't dream of closing them," Jane said, and she led the manager away, or rather furrowed a path for him, and I went for a drink. That was not easy. The table that had been set up as a bar was practically inaccessible, but I finally got to it. My wife, Liz, was there already and drunk, good and drunk.

"So here's Monte," she said. "The man's friend. Did all of you know that Monte is the man's friend? I'm Monte's friend too. I got news for you—when you got a friend like Monte, you don't need enemies."

People around smiled sheepishly, the way people do in such a situation. I had asked for a Scotch on the rocks but I was ready to force my way out of the place without it.

"Don't run away, Monte. I want you to meet my friends. Any friend of Andy's is a friend of mine, and there's no one here tonight but friends of Andy. Right? Right, Monte?"

I nodded. She put her arm around a slim, blond boy who could not have been more than twenty-three or twenty-four and who was dressed in a double-breasted mod suit of dark purple corduroy with brass buttons and skin-fit trousers. "This is David Dorchester. You pronounce it Dorster, don't you, lovey?"

"Oh, yes, yes—Dorster."

"He's just done the very best mod line in England and brought it over here. He's exploded into our stinking reality, haven't you, lovey?"

"Oh—yes, quite."

"Four pages in *Harper's Bazaar*, and you're a friend of Andy's—aren't you, lovey?"

"I admire him, of course. Read him and all that. Never met him. I would love to, really."

"See—he would love to, Monte. Monte is his beloved friend."

"How did you get here?" I asked him, if only to say something.

"Oh, Jerry brought me," he said, nodding at a small, fat man who stood beside him, nursing a drink and perspiring copiously. "Jerry's bought my line for America. Jerry has the mod field, and we'll all be frightfully rich out of it. That kind of opportunity in America. The old country is very stodgy, you know."

Jerry smiled and oozed perspiration, and Liz asked him, "And how did you get here, Jerry? Friend of Andy's?"

"Admiration, dear lady." He took out a handkerchief that was soaking wet and mopped his brow. "Admirer. His publisher is my brother-in-law."

I got my Scotch on the rocks and broke out of there, and pushed my way through to the terrace, where I stood and shivered. I have been married twenty-four years, if you are curious. No children. I stood and shivered and drank the Scotch. Joe Jacobs joined me there.

"Isn't this one hell of a party," he said. "You know, part of the cost ought to go on my swindle sheet. I will get three columns out of this and a couple of nights off the prowl. God bless you, Monte."

"I'm just a guest—same as you."

"Sure, sure—listen, Monte." He consulted his little notebook. "Andy and the governor. Governor: 'What are you writing now, Andy?' Andy: 'Nothing.' (I imagine he hates that question. It's a stupid question, and I guess every writer hates it.) Governor: 'Well—I mean what are you planning?' Andy: 'Nothing. I don't plan writing. You don't plan an act of creation. It explodes inside of you and burns your gut until you rid yourself of it.' Governor: 'I never experienced quite that.' Andy: 'You're rich. You have lots of things. Why the hell should you want creation? It's pain. People don't search for pain. They're burdened with it.' How about that, Monte?"

"I don't know. I can't say that I really know what he's talking about."

"Andy?"

"Andy—yes."

"You're a little fuzzy now."

"I've had one or two."

"Sure. Anyway, thank Andy, God bless him. I will try to quote him correctly. Tell him that. When I misquote him, he wants to tear me apart."

"I'll tell him that."

My glass was empty, and I fought my way back to the bar. Liz was not there; neither was the blond boy with the mod suit. I didn't see either of them again that night, and I hoped that the kid would please her and not turn out to be the way he looked.

8

At half past four in the morning, the party was over, and except for Andy's entourage, only the red-headed belly dancer remained. She was stretched out on the couch in the living room, out cold and snoring softly. Somehow you never connect snoring with a big, sexy kid like that. Jane Pierce had kicked her way out of the debris about a half hour before, leaving me with one final look of alcoholic hostility. She had everything that a woman could want—figure, looks, brains and success—but she loved no one. Jose Peretz was beginning to clean up.

"The hell with that," Andy said. "Let the chambermaids clean up. Get yourself a nightcap and turn in."

"I am no pig to wallow in litter."

Andy said something in quick Spanish, and then they both laughed.

"And keep your hands off that kid," Andy said, nodding at the belly dancer. "She's twenty years old and a silly little bitch, so just let her sleep it off in peace."

He had been drinking since he opened his eyes the day before; but he wasn't drunk, and his voice was steady and easy, and he didn't appear very tired. I was tired. I was as tired as death itself, and I had the taste of death in my mouth and in my heart. I went out onto the terrace to breathe a little fresh air. Diva was there. Over in Queens, there was a bluish-pink edge in the sky. The smell of the air was clean and damp, the way it is on a New York morning.

"Well?" Diva said to me. "You have good time at the party, Monte?"

I shrugged, and she said, "What kind of a man are you?"

"Your guess is as good as mine."

She spat over the terrace in a very expressive and Spanish gesture. Andy came onto the terrace and told her, "Leave him alone and go to bed, Diva. Haven't you any brains? Haven't you any goddamn brains at all?"

"Just be careful, hey, Andy," she whispered. "Just be careful and don't ever talk to me like this again."

Then she swirled off the terrace and we heard the door of her bedroom crash behind her. Andy looked at me and smiled thinly.

"What the hell, Monte."

I shrugged.

"So we don't do things very good. We don't write so good and we don't hunt so good and maybe we don't love so good either, and what the hell's the difference anyway! It was a hell of a party, wasn't it?"

"It was a good party."

"But you say hello too much. You give too much. You don't remember what you are—or maybe you never know. I begin to feel small and choked. Then I am lost. I want to sit down and cry. You know?"

"I know."

"Then why did you do it?" Andy asked me gently. "You didn't have to have her here tonight."

"I'm a masochist."

"Leave her, Monte."

"Then it hurts her and she cries and goes into a depression. I suppose I love her or something like that."

"Monte—I'm getting out of here. Tomorrow, the next day. I can choke here. Tell you what—I have a standing invitation from the Earl of Dornoch. He has seven thousand acres in the Highlands, high north—north enough so that at this time of the year there is no real night. Black Angus cattle and deer—the old English deer. Over a thousand deer run on his land. Have you ever been to Scotland?"

I shook my head.

"You can't imagine it—a tiny land with the widest vistas in the world. You stand on a mountaintop in the Highlands, and there's a kind of freedom wherever you look, an illusion of vastness. It's an old and wild and empty land, and you hunt there with a sense of others hunting before you, and it's a feeling you don't have anywhere else. It's something valid."

I shook my head.

"No. I thought not. You never hunted, did you, Monte?"

"No."

"Never wanted to?"

"No, I never wanted to, Andy."

"Why not?"

"I don't want to kill."

"On a moral basis, Monte?"

"I don't know. I never thought about it very much."

"Everything lives and dies, Monte. That's the definition of life. You're the hunter or the hunted. But in the hunt and in the kill, there is a kind of exultation. It's a moment of passion. How many moments of passion does life give you?"

"I'm just the guy to ask, Andy."

"I'm sorry. Think about it?"

"I'll think about it."

"Get some sleep. We'll talk tomorrow."

9

I walked home through a city of beginning dawn. The night workers were coming home, but the day workers had not yet appeared. Like myself, the night people were drawn and tired. I tried to remember what kind of deer one would find in Scotland. Would they be fallow deer? I seemed to recollect out of my boyhood reading that Robin Hood killed the fallow deer. Or was it the red deer? Was fallow a name of a species or simply a color? Would they be white deer or yellow deer? I made a note of that in the woolly drift of my thoughts and promised myself that I would ask Andy about it the following day.

Fortunately, we had no doorman. I let myself in with the common key, used the self-service elevator, and entered the four-room apartment that I called home. She wasn't there. I got out of my clothes, crawled under the covers and slept. It was a rotten sleep, filled with bad dreams, but I slept.

And then the phone rang. I heard Liz's voice. "Monte —for Christ's sake, will you get that phone!"

I looked at my watch: it said four o'clock, and since

the room was filled with daylight, it was obviously four
o'clock in the afternoon. I tried to fix the day, while the
phone rang a third and a fourth time.

"Will you get that son-of-a-bitch phone!"

Andy had come in on Friday—two o'clock in the afternoon on Friday—so this was Saturday.

"God damn you!"

Usually a phone will stop after three or four rings. I
picked this up on the seventh ring. I was still half asleep,
but when I heard Andy's voice, I became alert. His voice
was tense and hard, and he apologized for waking me, but
only to get that aside.

"What is it, Andy?"

"I'm in trouble," he said. "I am in damn big trouble,
Monte."

"Where are you?"

"In the phone booth at the St. Regis. In the King Cole
room. You know the booth at the far end of the room?"

I couldn't see how it mattered where the phone booth
was, but I told him I knew.

"That's where I am. In the phone booth."

"All right. Just take it easy." I could not have seen
myself telling Andy Bell to take it easy, but neither could
I have anticipated that a time would come when I would
hear this kind of tension and anxiety in Andy Bell's voice.

"Monte, I'm being hunted."

"What?"

Suddenly, his voice became quiet and controlled. "You
heard me, Monte. I am being hunted."

"How do you know?"

"Monte, goddam it, I am a hunter. I know."

"When did it start?"

"Two hours ago—when I left the Carlyle."

"Are you all right where you are?"

"I think so. I think I broke clear. But I have to talk to you about this. I have to talk to someone I can trust. I can trust you."

"Anyone recognize you there—at the bar, I mean?"

"No. I suppose that's a blow. Funny, I sit here, and under everything else I am scared shitless the way I was never scared before, and still I can feel the bruises on my ego because no one recognized me."

"You've been away a long time."

"Yeah. The bartender looked at me twice. I didn't want anybody to spot me—not now. Then he apologized. He thought I was Burt Lancaster. Can you imagine, Burt Lancaster."

"Well, that's flattering."

"I don't want flattery, believe me, Monte. How soon can you get here?"

"I got to wash and shave—say a half hour."

"Pare it a bit. I'll stay at the bar. God bless."

I put down the phone, and there was Liz at the door, not looking her best, with the day blinders hanging around her throat like some kind of pop art necklace.

"Who the hell was that?" she asked me.

"Andy."

"Buddy-boy. What did he want?"

I never could feel hostile enough to say that it was none of her damn business. I told her that Andy was in trouble, and then I went into the bathroom and began to shave. She followed me.

"Trouble. What kind of trouble is big enough for golden boy to wake us up like this?"

"He's being hunted."

"What? Who?"

"Andy."

"Andy's being hunted? Oh, no—no, I don't believe it."

"Well, that's what it is."

"You're not pulling my leg, Monte?" I didn't reply, and after a moment, she said, "What about you?"

"He wants me. He needs me."

"He's being hunted, and you're going to him?"

"That's right."

"You're not scared?"

"I'm so scared I can't hold this razor. I've cut myself twice already."

"Shmuck," she said. It was pretty ethnic for a woman who was part Irish, part Polish and a little Presbyterian. She could come up with the right word. I could not.

10

I found Andy at the bar in the St. Regis, and he took his drink to a table. He was holding a brandy, and mostly he was holding it and not tasting it.

"I can't drink," he said. "Do you want to order something?"

The waiter was hovering over us, so I sent him away for a dry vermouth on the rocks.

"The thing is," Andy said, "that I can't bear to have it on my tongue or my stomach. I tried. I figured I would get drunk."

"That's not easy for you."

"No, it's not."

"I've been thinking about it," I said. "I've been trying to work something out. I even thought of calling Jose and telling him to meet us here with one of your guns—or maybe that pistol you talked about."

"That would be stupid!" he snapped.

"I didn't do it."

"All right. I'm sorry. I'm tense and as I said, I am scared shitless. I wouldn't have said anything like that to you otherwise, Monte. You know that."

"I know that."

The waiter came with my drink. We were silent until he was gone, and then Andy said gently, "You see, Monte, it's no damn good to have a gun or anything like that. That's for the hunter. I'm the hunted."

"You're sure, Andy?"

"Oh, so right, Mr. Bell."

He nodded.

"I thought of something else."

"Oh?"

"Obvious. Not like some stupid notion about a gun, but just obvious."

Andy waited.

"Get away," I said. "You make a run for it. Out of the city. A long, clean run."

He was silent for a while, and then he shook his head.

"You said you were clear—you said you broke clean. This may be the only moment."

"I know."

"I got six hundred and change in my pocket. They know me at the desk. I could cash another two—three hundred there. It's no great stake, but along with a couple of charge cards, it can take you a long way."

He shook his head again. "Thanks."

"Why not?"

"I don't know. Pride."

"You're going to be brave," I said. "Jesus Christ, Andy, you're being hunted and you're going to be brave. You got to make a big score in opinion. For what?"

"It's hard to explain, Monte."

"You have to prove you're brave. I'm scared. I don't want to prove anything."

"I'm scared, Monte."

"And you won't run. My God, Andy," I begged him, "what else is there? What's the alternative?"

"I don't know. Maybe it was just too much for me alone. Maybe I don't know how to be alone. Maybe I don't know how to be hunted. Maybe it's something you have to learn. You don't have to stay with me, Monte."

"Go to hell."

A slim kid with heavy black glasses came over to the table and said, "I recognized you, Mr. Bell." He was so nervous from his own presumption that he could hardly speak. "I'm a researcher for *Life*. If I could get some kind of exclusive interview with you, it might be the turning point in my career. I know I got no call coming over and barging in on you like this. My name is Harry Belton. I guess you can see how scared I am—"

"I can see." Andy nodded, smiling slightly.

"But, you know—"

"I hate to send you away," Andy said.

"It's just a set of circumstances," I told the kid. "It's impossible now."

"I understand."

"Some other time. Not now."

"I understand," the kid repeated. "I just want to say that I am a great admirer of yours, Mr. Bell. I read one of your books when I was nine years old. I don't know whether I understood everything in it, but I read it through. I was only nine."

11

About Andy and myself—I met him in 1938 in Spain—I mean the first time that I ever met him and knew him, although I had heard about him. Moving back from a tour of the front lines, I was in a car with five other correspondents and one of them was Andrew Bell. The car was a big, yellow Buick touring car, a 1934, which was one of the best and most enduring Buicks ever built, and it took us east from the front over some of the worst roads I ever traveled. At one point, where the road was too narrow and too curved to pass another car, we found ourselves tailgating an old truck loaded with Republican soldiers back for leave. The truck appeared to have no springs left; it was a platform truck with gate sides and a couple of pieces of old rope backing it, and possibly good for two tons when new. Now there must have been thirty-five or forty soldiers packed into it—men full of laughter and pleasure at being alive and returning from the front, standing, most of them, swaying gaily with the truck's motion and singing the Spanish round about the farmer, the sheep and sodomy.

And then the truck driver, trying to demonstrate he could go along as briskly as we in the touring car, took a curve too fast and the truck went over. One moment a truckload of singing, happy soldiers on leave, and the next moment a hillside covered with broken, bleeding bodies, a burning truck, and the kind of horror that you do not want to witness twice.

The correspondent driving the Buick came down on the brakes very hard, and we skidded to a stop; and then we tumbled out of the car, and Andy raced to the scene of horror, myself behind him. He went to work with his first-aid kit, with torn shirts for bandages and tourniquets, with whatever he could put to use in stopping bleeding or holding a broken bone in place. I was behind him, and then I found myself assisting him and responding to his instructions; but when we turned back to the touring car for a moment, we discovered that the four other correspondents were standing at the edge of the road, watching, and preserving their bright, expensive Abercrombie uniforms in pristine spotlessness, free of nasty bloodstains and soot stains.

"Lousy bastards," Andy said. Those were the first words he ever addressed to me. That was how I met him.

Now he was still talking to the kid, because he didn't know how exactly to brush him off, and he couldn't say to the kid, "Look, kid, I'm being hunted. I'm not the hunter any more. I'm the quarry. I'm the game. Have you ever seen a fox run? Have you ever watched them beat the brush for hares? Have you ever watched a line of naked black men with drums run the lions? I'm being run—that way, and now I have gone to earth, and I am hiding for a little while." No, he could not say that or anything like that, so he continued to answer the kid's questions.

I got up and went to the phone. Andy hardly noticed. "Phone call," I said. He nodded. I closed the door of the booth behind me and then I dialed Pete's number. The bartender answered. I asked for Pete and then waited and cracked my knuckles and tried to get more control of myself and watched Andy talk to the kid. Finally, Pete's voice came through the phone, and I said to him:

"Pete, this is Monte—Monte Case. Andy's friend."

"Sure. Check. That was one hell of a party! Oh, Lord, that was a party! Where is my buddy-boy, sleeping?"

"No, he's awake."

"Oh, Jesus, he's nursing a head. Right?"

"No—not exactly."

"There's a man who can hold his liquor."

"Pete—he's in trouble."

"Who? Andy? Balls. If Andy wants the city, the

mayor will give it to him. What kind of trouble can Andy have? He ain't sick, is he?"

"He's not sick. Pete, this is confidential, between us. You and me. I'm swearing you to a confidence."

"Horse-shit! Andy knows me. He can trust me with his last dollar. Tell me he's a Russian spy. It dies with me."

"Listen to me, Pete," I begged him, feeling how enthralled he was becoming with the sound of his own voice. Pete was a man who loved best to listen to himself. He was talking to himself now and listening to himself. He had no idea what I was trying to say to him, until I put it flatly.

"Pete—Andy is being hunted."

"I say you can trust me with anything. With his life. I say Andy can trust me with his life, if it comes to that."

"Pete, did you hear me?"

"I heard you."

"I said that Andy is being hunted."

"Hunted? Who, Andy?"

"That's right."

"Crazy. It's crazy. You putting me on?"

"I am trying to make you understand that Andy is being hunted."

"But he's the hunter."

"Not now. Now he's the game."

"Andy? Andy Bell can take care of himself."

"No! Why don't you listen to me, Pete? Why don't you stop being a goddamn fool."

"Who the hell are you to—"

"All right, all right. I apologize. But, my God, I'm here with Andy and we've gone to ground, and maybe we've

shaken loose and maybe we haven't, but we have to have a
place to lay in and someone to cover us—"

"What are you suggesting, Monte?" He understood
me now. His voice was suddenly cold and flat.

"Give us cover."

"Here?" Pete asked evenly.

"That's right. You have an apartment there. You got
food and liquor—"

"Why don't Andy get out of town?" he interrupted.

"You know Andy. Andy can't run."

"Why don't he get it through his head that he's not
the hunter any more?"

"Will you give us cover, Pete?"

"What is this *us*?"

"I'm staying with him."

"You're a big hero, Monte. I am no hero. You know
how much it cost to run up this little shack of mine. Two
and a half long miles. Two million, five hundred thousand
dollars—American. And not my dough. I never saw that
kind of dough. This is stockholders' money. I'm a public
corporation—listed on the American Stock Exchange. Look
me up some day if you want to buy a nice investment.
Suppose you do—so I got a responsibility to you same as I
got to my other investors. It's not my place. It's a public
responsibility. I'm not some kind of stinking louse that's
pulling any rug from under you. I got responsibility—"

I spoke a four-letter word and hung up, and then I
went back to where Andy was still talking to the kid.

"Son," I said to the kid, "please blow. This is a lousy
night for what you want."

"I got more than I hoped for," the kid said.

"Good. Will you leave us alone then?"

"Sure," the kid said. He shook hands with Andy and thanked him, and then he walked over to the bar to scribble what he remembered into his notebook.

"Nice kid," Andy remarked.

"What made you come to a place like the St. Regis?" I asked him. "It's the one place in town where you got to be recognized. It's a wonder you haven't gathered a crowd already. You know that sooner or later a columnist or a *Variety* guy or one of the news guys cases the King Cole Room."

"I don't think that way any more. It's a long time since I've been to this city."

"All right. Where now?"

"Why don't we go over to Pete's," he said. "I hear that he keeps a six-bedroom apartment over the place. He could give us cover, and if we get there clean—well, maybe I'd have a chance."

"No."

"Why not?"

"It's a lousy idea," I said. "You're running scared. That's the only reason you come up with such a lousy idea."

"You're out of your mind, Monte."

"Sure."

"We go to Pete's. Suppose you go out and snare us a cab—"

"No!"

He stared at me strangely, and finally I said, "I just spoke to Pete. That's what I went to the phone for."

"Oh."

"We'll go back to Carlyle," I said. "As long as you got to be so stinking brave and stay here, we'll go back to where you got some clothes and friends and guns."

Staring at the table top, he muttered, "Guns are no damn good. How many times do I have to tell you that?"

"I know. I just think in patterns."

"I'm sorry. I keep jumping on you. Why don't you spit in my face and walk out of here?"

"Sure." I looked at him newly and said, "I'll do that some time. Remind me."

12

We walked north on Madison Avenue. It was Saturday, too early for dining and too late for strolling, and the shoppers had gone home too. The streets were empty. I glanced at Andy, and he was tense, alert, his eyes darting here and there.

"The game isn't brave," he said.

"The hunter is brave."

"Crap," he said. "Just pure crap, Monte."

Then we ran for cover, and we found the entrance to the subway under the front doorway of Bloomingdale's. In the subway, it was better. People in the subway didn't recognize Andy, and the subway was covered over, dark, a place to run to ground.

"But when you run to ground," Andy said to me,

"that's it, isn't it? Then it's over. Then you got a hole in the earth, and you stay there. You put your face on the ground. Do you remember what the ground feels like against your cheek, Monte, cold and wet?" A train pulled in and we got on, going uptown, north. The car was almost empty, and we sat down slowly, like strangers.

"I remember," I said.

At 77th Street, Andy got up to leave. I followed him. We stood on the platform until the train roared away uptown, and then the only sound was the grumbling distant noise that a subway always makes.

"What in hell is in it for you, Monte?" Andy asked me harshly.

"You wouldn't write it that way," I said to him. "You'd call me names and burn my ass a little, so I walk out on you. We don't want to go in for that kind of thing."

"I suppose not," he said. "If you want to stay, Monte, let's try to stop being afraid."

"We can try," I agreed.

13

At the hotel, outside of Andy's suite, a press delegation bigger than the one that had met him at the airport was waiting. The worried manager had told us that there were reporters upstairs, but we hadn't anticipated anything like this. A big feeder cable lay on the hallway floor, and maybe forty—fifty other wires as well, and there were TV cameras from the three big networks. There were newsreel cameras, hand cameras and a flock of reporters; and the moment Andy came in sight, the take began. The reporters crowded around, with the CBS microphone shoved close in, ABC and NBC flanking, and the NBC man alternating the questions with Frank Brady from *The New York Times*, and everyone else made notes and sparked the excitement. I didn't make any notes there, but it was pretty much as follows, checked against the *Times* story:

"When did you discover that you were being hunted, Mr. Bell?"

Andy could have told them to go to the devil and be damned, and what difference would it have made at that point? But instead he stood there, his hands in his pockets, towering over the lot of them and slouching slightly, and informed them quietly and politely that he had become aware of being the quarry only a few hours ago, early in the afternoon.

"And what did you do then Mr. Bell? What steps did you take?"

"I hid my trail as well as I could. I was in a snare of sorts then, but I broke out and found cover."

"What kind of cover?"

"It doesn't matter. I needed a place where I could sit and think."

"And how did you get back here?"

"Simple evasion. Nothing very clever."

"Will you be leaving New York now?"

"No."

"Why not?"

"I don't choose to."

"Then doesn't it follow—?"

"It follows."

"How does it feel to change places, Mr. Bell?"

"Lousy."

"But don't you feel that your skill as a hunter—?"

"No."

"But surely you don't consider yourself in the same position as any other man being hunted?"

"I do."

"Do you have any feelings of fear, Mr. Bell?"

"If it interests your readers, yes."

"Your reputation for courage—"

"A lie, like all other reputations."

"To get back to the question of evasion as a tactic, Mr. Bell—doesn't it follow that the only evasion that makes any sense is to leave the city?"

"I never was very sure of what makes sense."

"Yet you state emphatically that you will not run?"

Andy shrugged.

"Have you ever been hunted before?"

"No, this is the first time."

"Tiny Joe was on the air less than an hour ago, charging that this whole thing is a publicity stunt. Have you any comment to make about that, Mr. Bell?"

"No."

"Won't you please make a statement?" the NBC man pleaded. "Any kind of a statement. People want to know how you are taking this."

Andy shook his head.

"You have an obligation to the public, Mr. Bell."

"I am very tired," Andy said. "I think that's all for now."

I maneuvered him toward the door of the suite. Jose had the door open. We both slipped in, and Jose drove the door closed behind us. Andy flopped into a chair in the living room, and said to Diva, who was standing tensely at one side of the room:

"Diva, call the manager and tell him to clear them out of the hall. That's his obligation. I don't care how he does it, and I don't give a damn how they feel about it. I want to be able to come and go without fighting that line-up out there."

Diva nodded and went into the bedroom to make the call. Jose poured Andy a glass of brandy and said:

"Trouble—damn big trouble, hey Monte?"

"You can say that."

Andy stared at the brandy for a long moment; then he gulped it down and almost choked on it. He flung the glass away from him.

"I understand," Jose nodded.

"This crap that it's easy to die," Andy said. "This filthy crap that it's easy to die."

Diva came out of the bedroom. "I spoke to the manager. He'll do his best. He wants to stop by later and have a word with you. I tell him is all right—yes?"

"No. I don't want to talk to him."

"Have a word with him, Andy."

"You had a word with Pete."

"Then I'll talk to him," I said.

"No—the hell with that. I'll see him when he comes up."

"You want anything, Andy?" Diva asked him.

"No."

I walked out onto the terrace, and Diva followed me. The sun was setting over Queens. The city was quiet and lovely and full of shadows.

"I am a bitch, Monte," Diva said. "You are married to one. You need me like I need what happened today. I suppose you tell your wife. Oh, you shouldn't have, Monte. That's how they know."

"Maybe not. I had to tell Pete."

"Pete is a pig," she whispered. "Don't you know Pete is a pig?"

"He's Andy's friend."

"Oh, that's a stinking lie, number one. Friends! Andy has no friends. Jose and me—we are servants. That's better. And you—"

"Yeah—and me?"

"I don't know what you are. You asked Pete for shelter? You asked Pete for life?"

"He's a public corporation."

"You know what he is."

The doorbell rang, and Diva went inside to open the door. I followed. Andy sat in his chair without moving. It was the hotel manager. Diva let him in and closed the door quickly behind him. Jose pulled up a chair for him. He nodded at me and sat down facing Andy.

"I manage the place," he said to Andy. "It's a job."

"Why don't you tell me that you admire me?" Andy asked.

"I have too much respect for you to say that."

"Thank you," Andy said.

"Still—well, what do you say, Mr. Bell?"

"I don't think any harm will come to the hotel."

"Can you guarantee that?"

"You know better than to ask me that." Andy smiled.

"I have to ask it."

"I was a hunter," Andy said. "A hunter waits until the game moves into the open. Even when he spots the lair."

"Unless he becomes impatient."

"I'll make my run," Andy said. "I have to rest a little. I'm tired now. But I'll make my run."

"I heard you won't leave the city."

"I don't have to leave the city to make a run."

The manager watched Andy for a moment, saw him and appraised him. I liked the manager. "What the hell," the manager said, "it's only a job. Get your rest."

Then he left.

Andy closed his eyes. I went out onto the terrace, where the night was washing in. I stayed there for fifteen or twenty minutes, and then Andy called me.

14

"Sit down, Monte," he said.

I sat in the chair facing him.

"None of that crap I tried before. This is very simple

and direct. I am going to make a run for it. Get out and get clear."

"Tonight?"

"Tonight." Jose and Diva stood by the doors to the terrace, and Andy told them to clear out of the living room. "I want to talk to Monte alone." They went into their respective rooms, and I suppose they stood there with their ears against the doors.

"Why tonight?"

"I like the manager. I don't know what to say to you, Monte. I don't know how to thank you."

"For what?"

"Ah—I don't know. The hell with it. You get sentimental with someone like Pete. Right now sentiment would be offensive. It would offend you, wouldn't it?"

"It would offend me," I agreed.

"Then take off, Monte. For Christ's sake, take off."

Then I got up and left—without looking behind me and without saying anything else. Down in the lobby, I ran into the manager, and he said to me:

"Could I buy you a drink, Mr. Case?"

"If we don't talk about Andy Bell."

"I'll talk about running a hotel."

"You got me," I said.

I had three drinks and I learned a lot about running a large, posh, uptown eastside hotel, and then I shook hands with the manager.

"He'll make a run for it tonight, won't he?" the manager said.

"I guess so."

Out on the dark street, there was a cool breeze. The summer was almost done. It was a pleasant night. I thought about getting drunk, but the thought was not too pleasant. I thought about calling someone to have dinner with me, but first I called Liz. She wasn't home. Then I called a few people, but everyone knew about Andy being the quarry, and I was close enough to Andy for the people I knew not to desire closeness with me. Not on that evening anyway. I walked downtown and then I went into one of the flicks on Third Avenue, and I sat through a picture without knowing what went on in front of me and without being able to remember any of it; and then I walked over to the Oak Room at the Plaza and had a few more drinks and hoped that someone would happen by, but no one did. I went home then.

15

I slept badly. I dreamed and the dreams were not good, and then I woke up and lay in the dark and heard Liz come in; and then I must have dozed a little, because the telephone woke me at about six in the morning. It was O'Brian, from the Twenty-third Squad, and he told me about Andy.

"When?"

"Maybe twenty minutes ago. On Fifth Avenue, just south of the 56th Street corner."

"I'll be there."

"Good. That's good. I'll wait for you."

"What son of a bitch—" Liz began.

I put away the telephone and told her that Andy was dead.

"Oh, my God—"

It was no use to hurt her, and anything I would have said would have hurt her. It was never any use to hurt her; the world hurt her too much, and you would have to be a psychopath to add to it. I dressed and got down to 56th Street, and then I was sorry that I had been in such a damned hurry.

The hunt had finished there, and there was nothing recognizable left of Andy. What had been him was spread in a bloody smear halfway across Fifth Avenue, and the men from the morgue were trying to gather it up and make something in the way of remains out of it.

At this hour, on a Sunday morning, Fifth Avenue was all but deserted. The one or two citizens who came by did not stop. The smear was not something that anyone would want to stand around and look at.

O'Brian, who was supervising things, spotted me and came over with a handkerchief filled with the few possessions that had survived Andy—keys for doors I had never stepped through, some bills and some change, a crushed card case, a penknife, cufflinks bent shapeless, a broken pen —what could have belonged to Andy or to any other mortal man.

"I'm going to throw up," I said to him.

O'Brian nodded and led me over to a cardboard container that was conveniently waiting. Evidently, others had felt the same way.

(52

"Too much to drink last night."

"Sure," O'Brian said. "When did you see him last, Monte?"

"Last night at the Carlyle. At about eight or so, I guess."

"Did you know he would make a run for it?"

"He told me."

"Did you try to stop him?"

"Andy?"

"All right, but why did he stay in the city? Why didn't he break clear?"

I shook my head.

"Who are the next of kin, Monte?"

"One wife is dead. Another lives in Paris. The third lives in San Francisco and hates his guts."

"How about that Spanish dame and the little creep with the black polish hair?"

"They worked for him."

"Well, someone has to come over to the precinct with me," O'Brian said, "and sign papers and then go to the morgue and make arrangements."

"I'll do that."

"Funeral arrangements?"

"I'll start the ball rolling. I'll do what I can."

"My God," O'Brian said, "Andy Bell had enough friends. We certainly won't have any trouble in that department."

16

We didn't. Andy had been part Episcopalian, and the Rector of St. John the Divine suggested that the services be held there. Over three thousand people turned up, and the front part of the Cathedral contained about five percent of the best names in *Who's Who*, not to mention the *Blue Book*. Liz and I patched things up, and I dutifully put out two hundred and twenty-five dollars for the black ensemble she wore. She looked very attractive. I suppose a hundred people mentioned to me how attractive Liz looked. Diva and Jose were not there. They took off the same day Andy died, and no one ever saw them again or heard of them again, and the talk around was that they had robbed Andy of every nickel he had. But the truth of it was that every nickel he had was on him when he died, and his estate was deeply in debt, even though the royalties would pay off the debts in due time and show a handsome income eventually.

Andy's third wife's father had established a family plot in an Episcopalian cemetery out in the Hamptons. Strangely, with all that great crowd at the cathedral, only a handful drove to the cemetery: his third wife, her mother, myself and some cameramen. It was a pleasant day, and the cemetery was on a high, pretty, windy knoll. Liz was going to go out with me, but at the last moment she developed a migraine headache and had to go to bed.

The Trap

Chapter One

Bath, England
October 12, 1945

Mrs. Jean Arbalaid
Washington, D. C.

My dear Sister:

I admit to lethargy and perhaps to a degree of
indifference—although it is not indifference in your terms,
not in the sense of ceasing to care. I care for you very much
and think about you a good deal. After all, we have only
each other, and apart from the two of us, our branch of the
Feltons has ceased to exist. So in my failure to reply to three
separate letters, there was no more than a sort of inadequacy.
I had nothing to say because there was nothing that I wanted
to say.

You knew where I was, and I asked Sister Dorcas to
write you a postcard or something to the effect that I had
mended physically even if my brain was nothing to shout

about. I have been rather depressed for the past two months —the doctors here call it melancholia, with their British propensity for Victorian nomenclature—but they tell me that I am now on the mend in that department as well. Apparently, the overt sign of increasing mental health is an interest in things. My writing to you, for example, and also the walks I have taken around the city. Bath is a fascinating town, and I am rather pleased that the rest home they sent me to is located here.

They were terribly short of hospitals with all the bombing and with the casualties sent back here after the Normandy landing, but they have a great talent for making do. Here they took several of the great houses of the Beau Nash period and turned them into rest homes—and managed to make things very comfortable. Ours has a garden, and when a British garden is good, it has no equal anywhere else in the world. In fact, it spurred me to make some rather mawkish advances to Sister Dorcas one sunny day, and she absolutely destroyed my budding sexual desires with her damned understanding and patience. There is nothing as effective in cutting down a clean-cut American lad as a tall, peach-skinned, beautiful and competent British lady who is doubling as a nurse and has a high-bridged nose into the bargain.

I have been ambulant lately, pottering around Bath and poking my nose into each and every corner. The doctor encourages me to walk for the circulation and final healing of my legs, and since Bath is built up and down, I take a good deal of exercise. I go to the old Roman baths frequently, being absolutely fascinated by them and by the whole complex that is built around the Pump Room—where Nash and his pals held forth. So much of Bath is a Georgian city, perhaps more perfect architecturally than any other town in England. But there are also the baths, the old baths of the Middle Ages, and then the Roman baths which date back before that. In fact, the doctors here have insisted that I and other circulatory-problem cases take the baths. I can't see how it differs from an ordinary hot bath, but British physicians still believe in natural healing virtues and so forth.

Why am I a circulatory problem, you are asking yourself; and just what is left of old Harry Felton and what has been shot away and how much of his brain is soggy as a bowl of farina? Yes, indeed—I do know you, my sister. May I say immediately that in my meanderings around the town, I am permitted to be alone; so apparently I am not considered to be the type of nut one locks away for the good of each and everyone.

Oh, there are occasions when I will join up with some convalescent British serviceman for an amble, and sometimes I will have a chat with the locals in one of the pubs, and on three or four occasions I have wheedled Sister Dorcas into coming along and letting me hold her hand and make a sort of pass, just so I don't forget how; but by and large, I am alone. You will remember that old Harry was always a sort of loner—so apparently the head is moderately dependable.

It is now the next day, old Jean. October 13. I put the letter away for a day. Anyway, it is becoming a sort of epistle, isn't it? The thing is that I funked it—notice the way I absorb the local slang—when it came down to being descriptive about myself, and I had a talk with Sister Dorcas, and she sent me to the psychiatrist for a listen. He listens and I talk. Then he pontificates.

"Of course," he said to me, after I had talked for a while, "this unwillingness to discuss one's horrors is sometimes worn like a bit of romantic ribbon. You know, old chap—a decoration."

"I find you irritating," I said to him.

"Of course you do. I am trying to irritate you."

"Why?"

"I suppose because you are an American and I have a snobbish dislike for Americans."

"Now you're being tactful."

The psychiatrist laughed appreciatively and congratulated me on a sense of humor. He is a nice fellow, the psychiatrist, about forty, skinny, as so many British professionals are, long head, big nose, very civilized. To me, Jean, that is the very nice thing about the English—the sense of civilization you feel.

"But I don't want you to lose your irritation," he added.

"No danger."

"I mean if we get to liking and enjoying each other, we'll simply cover things up. I want to root up a thing or two. You're well enough to take it—and you're a strong type, Felton. No schizoid tendencies—never did show any. Your state of depression was more of a reaction to your fear that you would never walk again, but you're walking quite well now, aren't you? Yet Sister Dorcas tells me you will not write a word to your family about what happened to you. Why not?"

"My family is my sister. I don't want to worry her, and Sister Dorcas has a big mouth."

"I'll tell her that."

"And I'll kill you."

"And as far as worrying your sister—my dear fellow, we all know who your sister is. She is a great scientist and a woman of courage and character. Nothing you can tell her would worry her, but your silence does."

"She thinks I've lost my marbles?"

"You Americans are delightful when you talk the way you imagine we think you talk. No, she doesn't think you're dotty. Also, I wrote to her a good many months ago, telling her that you had been raked by machine-gun fire across both legs and describing the nature of your injuries."

"Then there it is."

"Of course not. It is very important for you to be able to discuss what happened to you. You suffered trauma and great pain. So did many of us."

"I choose not to talk about it," I said. "Also, you are beginning to bore me."

"Good. Irritation and boredom. What else?"

"You are a goddamn nosey Limey, aren't you?"

"Yes, indeed."

"Never take No for an answer."

"I try not to."

"All right, doc—it is as simple as this. I do not choose to talk about what happened to me because I have come to dislike my race."

"Race? How do you mean, Felton—Americans? White race? Or what?"

"The human race," I said to him.

"Oh, really? Why?"

"Because they exist only to kill."

"Come on now—we do take a breather now and then."

"Intervals. The main purpose is killing."

"You know, you are simply feeding me *non sequiturs*. I ask you why you will not discuss the incident of your being wounded, and you reply that you have come to dislike the human race. Now and then I myself have found the human race a little less than overwhelmingly attractive, but that's surely beside the point."

"Perhaps. Perhaps not."

"Why don't you tell me what happened?"

"Why don't you drop dead?" I asked him.

"Or why don't you and I occupy ourselves with a small pamphlet on Americanisms—if only to enlighten poor devils like myself who have to treat the ill among you who inhabit our rest homes?"

"The trouble is," I said, "that you have become so bloody civilized that you have lost the ability to be properly nasty."

"Oh, come off it, Felton, and stop asking for attention like a seven-year-old. Why don't you just tell me what happened—because you know, it's you who are becoming the bore."

"All right," I agreed. "Good. We're getting to be honest with each other. I will tell you—properly and dramatically and then will you take your stinking psychiatric ass off my back?"

"If you wish."

"Good. Not that it's any great hotshot story for the books—it simply is what it is to me. I had a good solid infantry company, New York boys mostly; some Jews, some Negroes, five Puerto Ricans, a nice set of Italians and Irish, and the rest white Protestants of English, Scotch, North of Ireland and German descent. I specify, because we were all on the holy mission of killing our fellow man. The boys were well trained and they did their best, and we worked our way into Germany with no more casualties or stupidities than the next company; and then one of those gross and inevitable stupidities occurred. We came under enemy fire and we called our planes for support, and they bombed and strafed the hell out of us."

"Your planes?"

"That's right. It happened a lot more often than anyone gave out, and it was a wonder it didn't happen twice as much. How the hell do you know, when you're way up there and moving at that speed? How do you know which is which, when one and all are trying to cuddle into the ground? So it happened. There was an open farm shed, and one of my riflemen and I dived in there and took cover behind a woodpile. And that was where I found this little German kid, about three years old, frightened, almost catatonic with fear—and just a beautiful kid."

I must have stopped there. He prodded me, and pointed out that the war had drawn small distinction between children and adults, and even less distinction between more beautiful and less beautiful children.

"What did you do?"

"I tried to provide cover for the child," I explained

patiently. "I put her in my arms and held my body over her. A bomb hit the shed. I wasn't hurt, but the rifleman there with me—his name was Ruckerman—he was killed. I came out into the open with the kid in my arms, warm and safe. Only the top of her head was gone. A freak hit. I suppose a bomb fragment sheared it clean off, and I stood there with the little girl's brains dripping down on my shoulder. Then I was hit by the German machine-gun burst."

"I see," the psychiatrist said.

"You have imagination then."

"You tell it well," he said. "Feel any better?"

"No."

"Mind a few more questions, Felton? I am keeping my promise to take my ass off your back, so just say No, if you wish."

"You're very patient with me."

He was. He had put up with my surliness and depression for weeks. Never lost his temper, which was the principal reason why he irritated me so.

"All right. Question away."

"Now that you've told this to me, do you feel any different?"

"No."

"Any better?"

"No."

"That's good."

"Why is it good?" I asked him.

"Well, you see—the incident outraged you, but not in

a traumatic sense. Apparently it doesn't hurt or help very much to recall it."

"It's not blocked, if you mean that. I can think about it whenever I wish to. It disgusts me."

"Certainly. As I said, I believe your depression was entirely due to the condition of your legs. When you began to walk, the depression started to lift, and they tell me that in another few weeks your legs will be as good as ever. Well, not for mountain climbing—but short of that, good enough. Tell me, Felton, why were you so insistent upon remaining in England for your convalescence? You pulled a good many strings. You could have been flown home, and the care stateside is better than here. They have all sorts of things and conveniences that we don't have."

"I like England."

"Do you? No girl awaited you here—what do you like about us?"

"There you go with your goddamn, nosey professional touch."

"Yes, of course. But, you see, Captain, you made your indictment universal. Man is a bloody horror. Quite so. Here, too. Isn't he?"

"Oh, do get off my back," I said to him, and that ended the interview; but by putting it down, "he said," "I said," etc., I am able, my dear Jean, to convey the facts to you.

You ask whether I want to come home. The answer is, No. Not now, not in the foreseeable future. Perhaps never, but never is a hairy word, and who can tell?

You say that my share of mother's estate brings me over a hundred dollars a week. I have no way to spend any of it, so let the lawyers piddle with it just as they have been doing. I have my own dole, my accumulated pay and a few hundred dollars I won playing bridge. Ample. As I said, I have nothing to spend it on.

As to what I desire—very little indeed. I have no intentions of resuming the practice of corporate law. The first two years of it bored me, but at least I brought to them a modicum of ambition. Now the ambition is gone, and the only thing that replaces it is distaste. No matter what direction my thinking takes, I always return to the fact that the human race is a rather dreadful thing. That is, my dear, with the exception of yourself and your brilliant husband.

I am better able to write now, so if you write to me and tell me what brilliance and benevolence you and your husband are up to now, I shall certainly answer your letter.

Thank you for bearing with me through my boorish months.

Harry.

Chapter Two

Washington, D. C.
October 16, 1945

CAPTAIN HARRY FELTON
BATH, ENGLAND

My dear Harry:

I will not try to tell you how good it was to hear
from you. I never was terribly good at putting my feelings
down on paper, but believe me I have read and reread your
letter, oh, I should say, at least half a dozen times, and I have
done little but think of you and what you have been through
and your situation at this moment. I am sure you realize,
Harry, better than anyone else, that this is not a time for
bright words and happy clichés. Nothing I say at this moment is going to make very much difference to you or to
your state of mind or, of course, to your state of health.
And nothing I offer at this moment in the way of philosophical argument is going to change any of your atti-

tudes. On my part, I am not sure that changing them at this moment is very important. Far more important is Harry Felton, his life and his future.

I have been talking about that to Mark and thinking about it a great deal myself. Harry, we're both of us engaged on a most exciting project which, for the moment, must remain surrounded with all the silly United States Army attitudes of secrecy and classification. Actually, our project is not military and there are no military secrets concerned with it. But at the moment we are operating with Army money and therefore we are surrounded with all sorts of taboos and rules and regulations. Nevertheless, Harry, rest assured that the project is fascinating, important and, quite naturally, difficult. We need help—I think specifically the kind of help you might provide. And at the same time, I think we can give you what you need most at this moment of your life—a purpose. We cannot give you a profession, and, when you come right down to it, we cannot ask you to be much more than an exalted messenger-boy—reporter. However, the combination of the two will give you a chance to travel, perhaps to see some of the world that you have not yet seen, and, we think, to ask some interesting questions.

Truthfully, our mission requires a very intelligent man. I am not apple-polishing or trying to cheer you with compliments. I am simply stating that we can make you a fairly decent offer that will take your mind off your present situation and at least give you an interest in geography.

At the moment we can pay you only a pittance, but you say in your letter that you are not particularly concerned with money. We will pay all expenses, of course, and you may stay at the best places if you wish.

Just as an indication of the kind of wheels we present-ly are and the kind of weight we can throw around, Mark has completed your discharge in England; your passport is on its way via diplomatic pouch, and it will be handed to you personally either before this letter arrives or no more than a day later.

The bit in your letter about your legs was reassuring, and I am sure by now you are even further improved. What I would like you to do, at our expense, is to pick up a civilian outfit. If you can buy the clothes you need in Bath, good; if not, you'd better run up to London and buy them there. You will want, for the most part, tropical, lightweight stuff since the wind is up for us in the Far East. Though you will travel as a civilian, we are able to offer you a sort of quasi-diplomatic status, and some very good-looking papers and cards that will clear your way whenever there is a difficulty about priorities. I'm afraid that priorities will remain very much in the picture for the next six months or so. We are short of air-travel space as well as of a num-ber of other things. But, as I said before, we are very large wheels indeed, and we envisage no trouble in moving you wherever we desire to. That's a dreadful thing to say, isn't it, and it almost places you outside of the picture as a human being with any volition of your own. Believe me, Harry, like your charming British psychiatrist, I am combining irritation with love. No, I know how easy it would be for you to say No, and I also know that a sharp negative will be absolutely your first and instinctive reaction. By now, of course, simply reading my letter you have said No half a dozen times, and you have also asked yourself just who the devil your sister thinks she is. My dear, dear Harry, she is a person who loves you very much. How easy it would be for me to say to you, "Harry, please come home immediately to the warmth of our hearts and to the welcome of our open arms." All too easy, Harry, and as far as I can tell, thinking the matter through, it would do you absolutely no good. Even if we could persuade you to come back stateside, I am afraid that you would be bored to tears and frustrated beyond belief. I think that I can understand why you do not want to come home, and I think that at this moment in your existence, it is a very proper decision for you to make. That is to say, I agree with you: you should not come home; but, at the same time, you must have something to do. You may feel, Harry, that this messenger-boy business is not the most creative thing in the world, but I think that rather than attempt to explain to you in advance what we are up to and what you will encounter, you should allow yourself to be drawn into it. You need make no absolute commitments. You will see and you will understand more and more, and at any point along the way you are free to quit, to tell us to go to the devil—or to continue. The choice is always yours; you have no obligation and you are not tied down.

On the other hand, this is not to say that we do not very much want you to accept the assignment. I don't have to tell you what Mark's opinion of you is. You will remember—and believe me it has not changed—he shares my love for you, and you command his very great respect along with mine.

Harry, if you are able to accept my offer, cable me immediately. I would like you to be ready to move out in the next day or two after cabling.

Meanwhile, you have all our love and all our best and deepest and most sincere wishes and prayers for a complete recovery. I do love you very much, and I remain,

Your most devoted sister,
Jean.

Chapter Three

By cable:

MRS. JEAN ARBALAID
WASHINGTON, D.C.
OCTOBER 19, 1945

THAT YOU SHOULD EVEN APOLOGIZE. I
ACCEPT YOUR OFFER WITH UNEQUIVOCAL
DELIGHT. ENTIRE OUTFIT AVAILABLE AT
BATH WHERE THE MEN'S HABERDASHERY
SHOPS ARE VERY GOOD INDEED. OUTFIT-
TING UP LIKE A VERY PUKKA EAST INDIAN
TYPE. READY TO LEAVE WHENEVER YOUR
SPECIFIC INSTRUCTIONS ARRIVE. THIS IS THE
FIRST TOUCH OF PLEASURE OR EXCITEMENT
THAT I HAVE EXPERIENCED IN A GOOD MANY
DREARY MONTHS. YOU AND MARK DEAR
SISTER ADMIRABLE PSYCHOLOGISTS. THANK
YOU BOTH. LOVE AND KISSES. I AWAIT
INSTRUCTIONS.

HARRY FELTON

By cable:

HARRY FELTON
BATH, ENGLAND
OCTOBER 21, 1945

THANK YOU HARRY AND OUR BLESSINGS
WITH YOU. AIR TRANSPORT FROM LONDON
AIRPORT ON 23 OCTOBER. SPECIAL PRIORI-
TIES TO CALCUTTA INDIA. AT CALCUTTA
PROCEED TO CALCUTTA UNIVERSITY AND
SEE THE INDIAN ANTHROPOLOGIST PRO-
FESSOR SUMIL GOJEE. QUESTION HIM. GET
ALL DETAILS INDIAN CHILD SUPPOSEDLY
STOLEN AND RAISED BY WOLVES VILLAGE
OF CHANGA IN ASSAM. STORY ASSOCIATED
PRESS REPORTER OCTOBER 9, 1945. ASSO-
CIATED PRESS STORY HAS PROFESSOR GOJEE
DEEPLY INVOLVED. PLEASE GET ALL DE-
TAILS AND WRITE FULL REPORT AS SOON
AS POSSIBLE.

JEAN ARBALAID

Chapter Four

BY AIRMAIL

Calcutta, India
November 4, 1945

MRS. JEAN ARBALAID
WASHINGTON, D.C.

My dear Sister:

First of all, I want you to know that I have taken your mission very seriously. I have never been contented with errand-boy status, as you will remember if you look back through the years of my life. Therefore, I decided to bring to the problem you set before me an observing eye, a keen ear, an astute mind, and all the skills of a poor lawyer. In any case, the mission has been completed, and I think that to some degree I have fallen in love with India. What a strange and beautiful place it is, especially now in November! I am told that in the summer months it is very different and quite unbearable. But my experience has been of a congenial climate and of a people as hospitable and gentle as I have ever known.

I arrived in Calcutta and saw the Indian anthropologist, Professor Gojee. We had a number of meetings, and I discussed this case with him quite thoroughly. I found him charming, intelligent and very perceptive, and he has been kind enough to have me at his house for dinner on two separate occasions, and to introduce me to his family. Let me tell you, indeed let me assure you, my dear sister, that in Bengal this is no small achievement.

But before I go into my discussions with Professor Gojee and the conclusions we came to, let me give you the general background of the matter.

The original Associated Press story seems to have been quite accurate in all of its details—so far as I can ascertain—and I have done my detective work thoroughly and assiduously. I went personally to the small village of Changa in Assam. It is not an easy place to get to, and requires plane, narrow-gauge train and ox cart. At this time of the year, however, it was a fairly pleasant trip. The village itself is a tiny, rather wretched place, but in Indian terms it is by no means the worst place in the world. It has what very few Indian villages have, especially in this part of Bengal—a tiny schoolhouse. It also has a schoolteacher and a number of people who are literate. This helps a great deal in the process of tracking down any historical data or events connected with the life and history of the village.

The village schoolmaster, whose name is Adap Chaterjee, was very helpful, since his English was excellent and since he knew all the participants in the particular event, and, indeed, was at the village when the child was originally lost. That was twelve years ago.

I am sure, Jean, that you know enough about India to realize that twelve is very much an adult age for a girl in these parts—the majority of them are married by then; and there is no question, none at all, about the age of the child. I spoke to the mother and the father, who originally identified the child by two very distinctive birthmarks. I saw these birthmarks myself in Calcutta, where the child is kept at the university. She has there at the university the best of care, kindness, and all the attention she demands. Of course, at this moment we cannot say how long the university will be able to keep her.

However, everything the mother and father told me about the child in the village of Changa seemed to be entirely compatible with the circumstances. That is, wherever their stories and the statements of other villagers could be checked, this checking proved that they had been telling more or less the truth—considering, of course, that any truth loses some of its vividness over a twelve-year period.

The child was lost as an infant—at eight months—a common story in these parts. The parents were working in the field. The child was set down and then the child was gone. Whether the child crawled at that age or not, I can't say, nor can I find any witness who will provide that particular information. At any rate, all agree that the child was healthy, alert and curious—a fine and normal infant. There is absolutely no disagreement on that point.

Now, I know full well that most European and American scientists regard the whole mythology of a child being raised by wolves or some other animal under jungle conditions as an invention and a fiction. But a great many things that Western science has regarded as fiction are now proving to be at least the edge of a fact if not the fact itself. Here in India, the child raised in the jungle is regarded as one of the absolutes of existence. There are so many records of it that it seems almost impossible to doubt it. Nor, as you will see, is there any other conceivable explanation for this child.

How the child came to the wolves is something we will never know. Possibly a bitch who had lost her own cubs carried the infant off. That is the most likely story, isn't it? But I do not rule out entirely any act of animosity against the parents by another villager. The child could have been carried off and left deep in the jungle; but, as I said, we will never have the truth on this question.

These wolves here in Assam are not *lupus*, the European variety, but *pallipes*, its local cousin. *Pallipes* is nevertheless a most respectable animal in size and disposition, and not something to stumble over on a dark night. When the child was found, a month ago, the villagers had to kill five wolves to take her, and she herself fought like a devil out of hell. At that point, the child had lived as a wolf for eleven years. This does not mean, however, that *pallipes* is a vicious animal. I recall reading a book not too long ago concerning the Canadian variety of *lupus*, the wolf. The naturalist commented on the fact that *lupus*, raised with a family as a dog might be raised, is, contrary to common legend, even more dependable and gentler than almost any house dog. The same naturalist goes on to say that all of the stories of *lupus* running in packs, viciously tearing down his prey, killing his fellow wolf in wolf-to-wolf fights—that all of this is invention, and not very pleasant invention. This naturalist said that there are absolutely no cases of interpack fighting among wolves, that they do not kill each other, and that they have taught each other and taught their offspring as great a responsibility as can be found in any species.

Personally, I would include man in that statement. My being here on this mission has led me to do a great deal of investigation and reading on wolves, and it all comes down to the fact that at this moment Harry Felton is ready to regard the wolf as an animal quite equal to, if not superior to, man in all moral and ethical behavior—that is, if you are willing to grant ethics to a wolf.

To get back to the problem we have here—namely, the story of this child's life among the wolves—will the whole story ever emerge? I don't know. To all effects and purposes she is a wolf. She cannot stand upright, the curvature of her spine being beyond correction. She runs on all fours and her knuckles are covered with heavy calluses.

One day at the university, I watched her run. They had put a heavy leather belt around her waist. From it a chain extended to a cable which, in turn, was anchored high up on two opposite walls of a room about twenty feet wide. While I observed her, this time for a period of about fifteen minutes, she ran back and forth the length of the cable, on all fours, using her knuckles as front paws. She ran back and forth in that swaying, horrible, catatonic manner that a caged animal comes to assume.

My first reaction to this was that they were being unduly cruel. Later I learned better. The fact of the matter is that, if anything, they are overly tender, overly gentle and thoughtful with her. It is in the nature of the educated Indian to have enormous reverence for all forms of life. The people at the university combine such reverence with great pity for this child and her fate. If you will remember, my dear Jean, your readings in Buddhism—specifically in the type of Buddhism that is practiced in Bengal—you will recollect that it teaches, among other things, the doctrine of reoccurrence. This means that this poor damned child is caught in an eternal wheel, destined to live this senseless, awful fate of hers over and over for eternity—or at least so they believe. And it evokes their great pity.

They have been trying for days to teach her to use her hands for grasping and for holding, but so far unsuccessfully. We are very glib when we talk of what man has done with a thumb in opposition to four fingers; but I assure you that in so far as this wolf-child is concerned, the thumb in opposition to her four fingers is utterly meaningless. She cannot use her thumb in conjunction with her fingers, nor can she properly straighten her fingers or use them in any way for any kind of manipulation—even for the very simple manipulation that her teachers try to lead her into.

Did I mention that she must be naked? She tears off any clothes they dress her in, and there are times when she will attack her leather belt with a kind of senseless ferocity. They attempted to put a cloth sleeping pad in the room, but in this they were unsuccessful, since she promptly tore to pieces each pad they placed there. They were equally unsuccessful in their attempts to teach her to defecate in toilet or chamber pot; in fact, any puppy is more easily housebroken than this child. Eleven years have given her a rigidity of action—or a mechanicality, as the university people here prefer to call it—which appears to preclude any kind of training.

However, the people at the university do not despair, and they hope that in time she will be able to master at least some elements of civilized behavior.

At this point, however, she has not been able to grasp even the meaning of speech, much less make any progress herself in the art of conversation or communication. The problem of communication with this child is absolutely staggering.

The Indian anthropologist, Professor Sumil Gojee (the man you had been in communication with), is very highly regarded both here and in Bombay, where he has been a guest lecturer on one occasion or another. He is a social anthropologist, you know, and he is recognized as a great authority on village life in Bengal. He has been working with the wolf-child for a week now, and during the past four days he has been joined by Professor Armen Ranand from the University of Bombay. Both of them have been very kind to me and have given me unstintingly of their time, which I want you to know is an achievement on my part, since I was unable to explain to them in any coherent fashion just what you are up to and after. That comes back to the fact that I am entirely ignorant of what you are up to and after, and have been able only to guess and to form some rather silly theories of my own which I will not bore you with.

At this point, both men have little hope that any real communication will ever be possible. In our terms and by our measurements, the wolf-child is a total idiot, an infantile imbecile, and it is likely that she will remain so for the rest of her life. This prognosis of mental rigidity puzzled me, and I discussed it at some length with both Professor Gojee and Professor Ranand.

Our first discussion took place while we were observing the child in her room, which has become for the most part her habitat. Do not think that she is held prisoner there in some heartless manner. She is taken for walks, but that is not easy; she is a rather savage little animal, and a great many precautions must be taken every time she is removed from her room. The room is equipped with one of those mirrors that enable you to look into it without being perceived from the inside. The mirror is placed high enough on the wall not to bother the child, and so far as I know she has never become aware of either the mirror or its two-way quality. Watching her on this occasion, Professor Gojee pointed out to me that she was quite different from a wolf.

I said to him, "I would think that being so unhuman she would at least be wolflike in most ways."

"Not at all," Gojee replied. "In the first place, she is twelve years old, which is very old indeed for a wolf. Do you understand? She has spent a lifetime, a wolf lifetime, among the wolves, during which her wolf companions have matured and, I imagine, in many cases gone to their deaths. She, however, remained through that period a child. Now you must not believe for a moment that she could have been unaware of her difference from the wolves. She was most aware of the difference, and indeed the wolves were also aware of this difference. The fact that they accepted her, that they fed her, that they took care of her, does not mean that they were foolish enough to mistake her for a wolf. No, indeed! They knew that they were dealing with a very nonwolf type of child; and I am inclined to believe that within the limitations of their mentality the wolves had some hazy notion that this was a human child. This could only have meant that she would be treated differently from the rest of the wolves, and the result of this different treatment would be a series of traumas. In other words, a wolf brought up in a normal wolf environment would, we could expect, be fairly free from neuroses. Now, this is probably a very silly use of terminology. We do not know whether neuroses exist among wolves, and we are not absolutely certain as to the nature of neuroses in the human being. However, we can with some certainty make a case for the neurosis of this child. Whether she is pathological, I am not certain, but certainly her emotional structure has been deformed beyond repair, and her intellectual powers have been stunted beyond belief and deprived of any ability to mature."

"Then what exactly is she?" I asked him.

He turned to Dr. Ranand and, with a rather sad smile,

repeated my question. Dr. Ranand, the professor from Bombay, shrugged his shoulders.

"How can I possibly answer that? She is not human; she is not a wolf. If we were to approach her in terms of her intelligence, then certainly we would say that she is closer to the wolves. But a wolf's intelligence is a completed thing; in other words, a wolf is just as intelligent as a wolf should be. Whether she is as intelligent as a wolf should be, I don't know. Presumably a wolf with her cranial capacity would be capable of a great deal of learning. She, on the other hand, is not capable of the kind of learning we would expect from this theoretical but nonexistent wolf with a super-large cranial capacity. What, then, is the poor child? A human being? No, I don't think she is a human being. A wolf? Quite obviously she is not a wolf." His voice trailed away here. He looked at Professor Gojee helplessly.

"We can conclude this," Professor Gojee said, "she has been denied the opportunity to become a human being."

The next day, a Dr. Chalmers, a British public-health officer, joined us for a period of observation. Like myself, he had been to the village of Changa, investigating her background. He bore out what I had learned there, that there was absolutely no history of imbecilism in her background. Afterwards, he was able to examine the child very carefully. I must say here, Jean, that in order for him to make this examination the child had to be put to sleep. Ether was used, and every care was taken. An anaesthetist from the General Hospital here administered the anaesthesia—under difficult conditions, I will admit. Then the child was unchained and was taken to a medical examination room where Dr. Chalmers conducted his physical examination under the supervision of both Professor Gojee and Professor Ranand. He found absolutely no physical elements to account for the child's mental condition: no malformation of the cranial area and no signs of imbecilism. His findings bore out my own in Changa; that is, the fact that everyone in the village had attested to the normalcy—indeed, alertness and bright-ness—of the infant. Both Dr. Chalmers and Professor Gojee made a special point of the alertness and adaptability that the infant must have required to enable it to begin its eleven years of survival among the wolves. The child responds excellently to reflex tests, and neurologically, she appears to be sound. She is also strong—beyond the strength of a normal twelve-year-old, indeed beyond the strength of most adults—very wiry, quick in her movements, and possessed of an uncanny sense of smell and hearing.

I watched while the doctor examined the wolf marks upon her—that is, the specific physical idiosyncrasies that were the result of her life among four-legged animals. Her spine was bent in a perpetual curvature that could not be reversed—even with an operation. Her calluses were well developed and most interesting; evidently she ran mostly, if not always, on all fours. Her teeth were strong and there were no signs of decay, although the incidence of tooth decay is rather high in the native village. While Dr. Chalmers is not a psychiatrist, his experience in the Public Health Service has been long and very varied; and, in his opinion, the prognosis for this child is not hopeful. Like Professor Gojee, he does not believe that she will ever progress to a point where she can master even the simplest use of language.

Professor Ranand believes that eventually the child will die. He has examined records of eighteen similar cases. These eighteen cases were selected from several hundred recorded in India during the past century. Of these several hundred recorded cases, a great many could be thrown aside as fiction. The eighteen cases Professor Ranand chose to study carefully were cases which he believed had been documented beyond a possibility of doubt. In every case, he says, the recovered child was an idiot in our terms—or a wolf in objective terms.

"But this child is not a wolf, is she?" I asked him.

"No, certainly not, by no means. The child is a human child."

"An imbecile?" I asked him. "Would you call the child an idiot? Would you call the child a moron? If you did, would you give her any number on the scale of intelligence we use?"

Professor Ranand was upset by this kind of thing and he brushed it aside, and he had some very harsh things to say about our Western methods of measuring intelligence.

"Of course the child is not an idiot," he said; "neither is the child an imbecile. You cannot call the child an imbecile any more than you would call a wolf an idiot or an imbecile because the wolf is not capable of engaging in human actions."

"But the child is not a wolf," I insisted.

"Of course not. We went over that before. The child is not a wolf, not by any means. Then you must ask what the child is and that, too, we have gone over before. It is impossible to state what this child is. This child is something that nature never intended. Now, to you, to you Westerners, this is a clinical point of view, but to us it is something else entirely. You do not recognize any such things as intentions on the part of nature. In so far as your Western science is concerned, nature moves blindly and mechanically with neither purpose nor intent nor direction. I think you have all driven yourselves into blind alleys with your concepts of the origin of the species. I am not arguing with Darwin's theories; I am only saying that your use of Darwin's theories has been as blind as your overall attitude toward the world and the life of the world."

Two days have passed since I wrote that section of my report which you have just read. Yesterday the wolf-child came down with some sort of amoebic dysentery. She seems entirely unable to fight the disease and she is obviously growing weaker. I will send you news as her condition changes.

Meanwhile, I am putting together all of the notes and the verbatim records of conversations that I have taken down concerning the wolf-child. When I have them in some proper and understandable form, I will send them to you. I don't know why this whole experience has depressed me as it has. My spirits were quite high when I arrived in India, and the whole business around this poor child has been, from my own selfish point of view, consistently interesting. At the same time, I made some good friends here, and the people at the university, the native Indian professors as well as the British here, could not have been kinder to me. I have every reason, my dear sister, for saying that I have enjoyed my stay in Bengal—but, at the same time, I feel a terrible sense of tragedy around this child, a sense of tragedy that goes far beyond her own piti-ful fate and her own personal tragedy. Perhaps when I work this out in my mind, I will be able to turn it into something constructive.

In any case, be assured that I am your errand boy for as long as you desire. I am intrigued by this matter, and I spend the pre-sleep hour each night guessing what you are up to, what your purpose is, and what you and Mark have in those cunning little scientific minds of yours. I have made some absolutely fascinating guesses, and if you are very nice to me perhaps I will pass them on to you.

Love and kisses,
Harry.

Chapter Five

By cable:

MRS. JEAN ARBALAID
WASHINGTON, D.C.
NOVEMBER 7, 1945

TODAY AT TWO O'CLOCK OUR TIME HERE
THE WOLF-CHILD DIED. THE DIRECT CAUSE
OF HER DEATH WAS THE DYSENTERY. THAT
IS THERE WAS NO WAY TO STOP THE DE-
HYDRATION OF THE CHILD WHICH CON-
TINUED TO A POINT WHERE SHE COULD
NO LONGER SUSTAIN HER LIFE. HOWEVER
DR. CHALMERS WHO IS BY NO MEANS A
MYSTIC BUT A VERY PRACTICAL BRITISH
PRACTITIONER FEELS THAT ALMOST ANY
INFECTIOUS DISEASE WOULD HAVE LED TO
THE SAME RESULT. SHE HAD BEEN DI-
VESTED OF ANY DESIRE TO LIVE AND IN
HER OWN WAY HAD BEEN IN VERY DEEP

DEPRESSION SOMETHING I RECOGNIZE AND
SYMPATHIZE WITH WHOLLY. I AM SENDING
THIS CABLE COLLECT AND AM MAKING NO
EFFORT TO ECONOMIZE WITH WORDS. I
AM SURE YOU CAN AFFORD IT. WHAT
NOW? I AWAIT WORD FROM YOU AT THE
HOTEL EMPIRE CALCUTTA.

HARRY FELTON

By cable:

HARRY FELTON
HOTEL EMPIRE
CALCUTTA, INDIA
NOVEMBER 9, 1945

YOU HAVE DONE SUPERBLY HARRY AND WE
ARE DEEPLY APPRECIATIVE. HOWEVER YOUR
REPORTS ARE TOO MODEST. WE LOOK UPON
YOU AS AN INTELLIGENT AND WELL-IN-
FORMED PERSON AND WE ARE VERY EAGER
FOR YOUR OWN REACTION. PLEASE REMAIN
IN INDIA AT HOTEL EMPIRE FOR TIME BEING
AND WRITE US IMMEDIATELY AIRMAIL YOUR
REACTION TO THE CHILD AND YOUR EXPLA-
NATION OF WHAT HAPPENED TO THE CHILD.
THIS IS TO BE ABSOLUTELY YOUR OWN EX-
PLANATION AND IF POSSIBLE NOT TEMPERED
OR BIASED IN ANY WAY BY THE SPECIALISTS
YOU HAVE DISCUSSED THE CASE WITH.

JEAN ARBALAID

Chapter Six

BY AIRMAIL

Calcutta, India
November 10, 1945

MRS. JEAN ARBALAID
WASHINGTON, D.C.

My dear Jean:

I am flattered by your interest in my opinion. On the other hand, I am not going to negate the value of such an opinion. I think I agree with you that professional people, specialists in one branch or another of the various sciences, tend to have a narrow point of view and tend very much to limit their statements to areas where they have either a background of experimental evidence or specific existing evidence upon which to base their assertions and conclusions. This is a very admirable and careful method in so far as it goes, but I am afraid it will achieve only what the facts at hand—that is, the provable facts—allow it to achieve.

I can guess that by now you have consulted every

available specialist on the question of human children being reared by animals. I am sure you have discussed this thoroughly with the bigwigs at the National Geographic Society and with all the various specialists who know more about animals than the animals know about themselves. Do they all agree that no human child was ever reared by so-called beasts? Do they all agree that the whole thing is a sort of continuing invention, a fiction that each generation perpetuates to confuse itself? If they do, they are in agreement with your Western naturalists here in Calcutta. I have spoken to three of them—two Englishmen and a Frenchman—and they are all absolutely certain of the scientific and historical ground they stand on. The wolf-girl is a fraud; she was not raised by the wolves; she is an idiot child who ran away from the village and spent perhaps weeks, perhaps months, wandering in the forest, deranged and developing calluses where the calluses are. And the odd thing, my dear Jean, is that I cannot prove differently. So much for evidence.

Now, as to my own conclusion which you asked for: I told you in the previous letter that I had been deeply depressed by the incident of this child and by her condition. I have been attempting to understand the origin of this depression in myself and to deal with it—if only to repay an obligation and a promise to a skinny British psychiatrist who pulled me out of the doldrums back in Bath. I think I have found the source of the depression—a sort of understanding of what the girl was afflicted with. I believe she was afflicted simply with the loss of humanity. Now you have every right to say that the loss of humanity is a widespread disease that afflicts most of the human race; and there I cannot argue with you. But, regardless of how much or often we turn into killers, mass murderers, sadists, etc., we seem always to preserve some sense of our origin, some link with our beginnings. We are at least recognizable as Homo sapiens. This child, poor thing, cut all her connections. She is no longer recognizable as Homo sapiens. Having the form of a human being, she is less than a human being, less indeed than what nature intended her to be.

I am quite impressed by the outlook of Professor Gojee and his associates. I think I must agree with their opinion of Western science. The sad fact is that, while the East is ahead of us in many ways, they have lagged behind in scientific method and discoveries; and therefore, the great intuitive feelings that they have and which they incorporate into some of their religion, concerning the meaning and the destiny of mankind, have remained disassociated from any wide discipline of fact and investigation.

For myself, I tend to agree with them that there must be some purpose to human existence. I am hesitant to ascribe such purpose to the presence of some omnipotent being who will fulfill our definition of God. I think that their definition and concept is as limited by our intelligence and as constrained by our outlook as most of our other theories. But, speaking only for myself, I have never been truly aware of the essence of humanity until I was present here at a case where humanity was extracted from a human being. We are too pat with our descriptions, designations and accusations of those whom we consider devoid of humanity. I don't really believe that anyone is devoid of humanity in the sense that this poor little wolf-child was. But then that leads me to another question. What is your human being? What is the essence of being human?

I have not been quick to embrace the all-encompassing theories of environment that have come out of the democratic movement of the nineteenth century. Too often I have felt that theories of environment have been used to prove political points and to make for political ammunition. At the same time, heredity is possibly less important than many people imagine it to be. I think that to create a human being, you need the presence, the society and the environment of other human beings. Directly to answer the question you put to me—What happened to the child? —I would say that she was deprived of her humanity. Certainly, she is not a human being, and neither is she a wolf. A wolf society can produce wolves; a human society can produce human beings. A human being trapped in a wolf society is a good deal less than a human being and perhaps not as much as a wolf. So I would say that this child occupied a sort of limbo on the scale, or in the current, of evolution. She is not a part of development; she is not a thing in herself; she is something that had been destroyed by a set of circumstances; she is a spoiled mechanism that continued to function in a limited sort of way. Do you find that a rather dreadful definition—a spoiled mechanism? Perhaps the word "mechanism" is wrong. Would a spoiled bit of life be better? I don't know, but there are my opinions for what they are worth.

I have found a charming young lady, Miss Edith

Wyckoff by name, who is the daughter of the colonel of an old Indian regiment. The whole thing is a cliché except that she is charming and blue-eyed, and will make the hours here, while I wait for your reply and for your instructions, much more endurable.

Please allow me to continue as your free-wheeling, theorizing errand boy. As the above demonstrates, my state of mind is infinitely better. I send my love to both of you, and await your reply.

Harry.

Chapter Seven

By cable:

HARRY FELTON
HOTEL EMPIRE
CALCUTTA, INDIA
NOVEMBER 14, 1945

THANK YOU FOR EVERYTHING HARRY. YOU
HAVE DONE NOBLY AND YOUR CONCLUSIONS
HAVE BEEN READ AND REREAD AND DIS-
CUSSED SERIOUSLY AND WITH THE GREATEST
OF INTEREST. A SIMILAR CASE HAS CROPPED
UP IN PRETORIA UNION OF SOUTH AFRICA AT
GENERAL HOSPITAL THERE UNDER DR. FELIX
VANOTT. WE HAVE MADE ALL ARRANGE-
MENTS WITH AIR TRANSPORT AND YOU WILL
BE WHISKED THERE BEFORE YOU CAN SAY
JACK ROBINSON. DREADFULLY SORRY TO
END ROMANCE WITH THE COLONEL'S DAUGH-
TER BUT IF YOU ARE VERY SERIOUS ABOUT IT
AND DESPERATE TO CONTINUE IT WE WILL
ARRANGE FOR YOU TO PICK IT UP LATER.
MEANWHILE ON TO PRETORIA.

JEAN ARBALAID

Chapter Eight

BY AIRMAIL

Pretoria, Union of South Africa
November 18, 1945

MRS. JEAN ARBALAID
WASHINGTON, D.C.

My dear Sister:

You are evidently very big wheels, you and your husband, and I wish I knew just what your current experiment adds up to. I suppose that in due time you'll see fit to tell me. Meanwhile, my speculations continue.

But in any case, your priorities command respect. A full colonel was bumped, and I was promptly whisked away to South Africa, a beautiful country of pleasant climate and, I am sure, great promise.

I saw the child, who is still being kept in the General Hospital here; and I spent an evening with Dr. Vanott, an entire day at the hospital, and another evening with a young and attractive Quaker lady, Miss Gloria Oland, an anthropologist working among the Bantu people for her doctorate. Her point of origin is Philadelphia and Swarthmore College, so I was able to play upon all the bonds that unite countrymen (I will have something to say about that later). But I think that my acquaintance with Miss Oland has been fruitful, and, all in all, I will be able to provide you with a certain amount of background material.

Superficially, this case is remarkably like the incident in Assam. There it was a girl of twelve; here we have a Bantu boy of eleven (an estimate). The girl was reared by a variety of wolf; the boy in this case was reared by baboons—that is, supposing that here, as in India, we can separate fact from fiction, and come to a reasonable assumption that the child actually was stolen and reared by baboons. Let me say at this point that I have done some investigating, and I have been able to add to my notebook over twenty cases of African children stolen by baboons or by some other kind of baboonlike ape and reared by said baboons and apes. Now these cases are by no means researched; they have not been tracked down; they have not been proven: so along with their interest as background material must go the assumption that most, if not all of them, belong to the mythology. However, if I have been able to turn up this number of cases in so short a time, and by asking as few questions as I did and of as few people, then it seems to me that this kind of thing must be fairly widespread throughout South Africa. Even if the overwhelming majority of stories belong to the mythology, any such mythology must have some basis in fact, however small.

The child was rescued from the baboons by a white

hunter, name of Archway—strong, silent type, right out of Hemingway. Unfortunately, unlike most of his fictional counterparts, this Ned Archway is a son of a bitch with a nasty temper and a thoroughgoing dislike for children. So when the boy understandably bit him—for which the boy can only be praised—the white hunter whipped the child to within an inch of his life.

"Tamed him," as Mr. Archway put it to me in one of the local bars over a tall mint julep. Archway is a thoroughgoing gentleman when he is with his betters, and, as much as I dislike that kind of talk, namely, "his betters," it is the only kind that fits. Back home, a sensitive person would catalogue Archway as poor white trash. I think that describes him better than several pages of words.

I asked him for some of the details of the capture and Archway swore me to silence, since evidently his actions were somewhat illegal. He loves to shoot baboons; it proves him "a target master," as he puts it.

"Shot twenty-two of the bloody beasts," he said to me.

"You're a very good shot," I said to him.

"Would have shot the little black bastard too," he added. "However, he awakened my curiosity. Nimble little creature. You should have seen him go. You know, I have one of your jeeps—marvelous car, marvelous for the bush country, kind of car that might have been made for this part of Africa. Well, I was in the car and I had with me two of your American women, two of your very rich women—you know the type: brown as smoked goose, long legs drawn hard and thin, and just couldn't wait for the war to be over to get out here on safari. They enjoyed the chase no end. Ran the thing down in the jeep. You know,

I don't think I would have ever gotten him if it weren't
that the jeep threw a bad scare into him, and he froze.
Animals do that, you know."

"He is not an animal," I ventured.

"Oh, of course he is. The Kaffirs are not so different
from the baboons anyway, when you come right down
to it."

This and a lot more. My conversation with the white
hunter was not pleasant, and I don't enjoy repeating it.

May I say that at the hospital here they have a more
humane, if not a more egalitarian, point of view. The
child is receiving the very best of care and reasonable,
scientific affection. I asked them at the hospital whether
there was any way to trace him back to his point of origin,
that is, to his parents or to the village where he originated.
They said No, there was no way at all of doing so, not in
a thousand years. Evidently these Basutoland baboons are
great travelers, and there is no telling where they picked
up the child. It might be several hundred or a thousand
miles away.

Putting his age at eleven years is a medical guess, but
nevertheless reasonable. That he is of Bantu origin there
is no doubt; and if I were to put him up as a physical speci-
men alongside of the white hunter, there is no doubt in my
mind who would come out best. The child is very handsome, long-limbed, exceedingly strong, and with no indication of any cranial injury. His head is narrow and long,
and his look is intelligent. Like the girl in Assam, he is—
in our terms—an idiot and an imbecile, but there is nevertheless a difference. The difference is the difference be-

tween the baboon and the wolf. The wolf-child was incapable of any sort of vocalization. Did I mention that at moments of fear she howled? In her howling she was able to give an almost perfect imitation of a wolf's howl— that is, the howl of the local wolf whose habitat is Assam. Aside from this howl, her vocalization was limited to a number of wolf sounds—barks, whines and that sort of thing. Here we have something different indeed.

The vocalization of this eleven-year-old Bantu boy is the vocalization of a baboon. Strangely enough, at least here in Pretoria, there is no indication of any local scientific and serious work being done on the question of baboon vocalization. Again, all we have is a variety of opinion based in mythology. Some of the Kaffirs here will swear that the baboons have a language. Others claim to know a little of the baboon language, and I have had some of the Kaffir hunters make an assortment of sounds for me— after I had paid them well—and proceed to state their own interpretations of what these sounds meant. I think this is less a tribute to the speech abilities of the baboon than to the ingenuity of the local Kaffir when it comes to extracting money from a white man. Miss Oland pooh-poohs any suggestion that the baboons have a language, and I am inclined to go along with her.

There is one reasonably well informed naturalist at the local college with whom I had a short chat over the luncheon table. He, too, derides the notion that there is a language among the baboons. He raises an interesting point, however. He believes that the ability to talk is the motivating factor for man's becoming man, and he also believes that certain frontal sections of the brain are absolutely necessary before a species can engage in conversation. He says that the only species on earth that has any sort of conversational powers whatsoever is man, and he proceeded to break down for me various theories that bees and other insects and some of the great apes can talk to each other. He said that there is a very strong myth in gorilla country that the gorillas are able to talk to each other, but this, too, he rejects unconditionally.

He does admit that there is a series of specific sounds that the gorillas use; but these sounds are explosive grunts used entirely for situations of danger. Each and every one of these sounds relates to some area of fear, and my naturalist cannot include them in what we understand as language. He is willing to admit, however, that the baboons have a series of squeaks and grunts that may communicate, in addition to situations of fear, situations of affection. I am inclined to agree with this, for there seem to be some indications that this Bantu child will in time learn at least some elements of speech.

In that way he differs from the wolf-girl, and he also differs from her in that he is able to use his hands to hold things and to examine things. He also has a more active curiosity, but that, I am assured by the naturalist, is the difference between wolf and baboon. The baboon is a curious creature, endlessly investigative, and he handles an endless number of objects. So the boy's curiosity and his ability to grasp things with his hands are an indication of his relationship to baboons, I think, more than an indication of his relationship to mankind.

As with the wolf-child, he too has a permanent curvature of the spine. He goes on all fours as the baboons do, and the backs of his fingers, specifically the area of the first knuckle joint, are heavily callused. After tearing off his clothes the first time, he accepted them. This, too, is quite different from the case in India, and here again we have a baboon trait. Miss Oland told me of cases where baboons have been trained to wear clothing and to do remarkable tricks. Miss Oland has great hope for the boy's progress in the future, but Dr. Vanott, who has worked with him and tested him in the hospital, doubts that the child will ever talk. How much Dr. Vanott is influenced by local attitudes toward Negroes, I leave for you to decide. Incidentally, in those numerous reports of human children raised by animals, which Professor Ranand of Bombay University professed to believe, there is no case where the child was able subsequently, upon being recovered and brought back into the company of human beings, to learn human speech.

So goes my childhood hero, Tarzan of the Apes, and all the noble beasts along with him. Poor Lord Graystoke. He would have been like this Bantu child—trembling with fear, never released from this fear, cowering into a corner of his cage, staring at his human captors with bewilderment and horror. Has it been said to you that animals do not experience fear in the sense that we human beings do? What nonsense! Fear appears to be woven into the fabric of their lives; and the thing that is most heartbreaking in both of these cases is the constant fear, the fear from which neither child was apparently free, even for a moment.

But the most terrifying thought evoked by this situation is this: What is the substance of man himself, if this can happen to him? The learned folk here have been trying to explain to me that man is a creature of his thought, and that his thought is, to a very large extent, shaped by his environment; and that this thought process—or mentation as they prefer to call it—is based on words. Without words, thought becomes a process of pictures, which is on the animal level and rules out all, even the most primitive, abstract concepts.

In other words, man cannot become man by himself: he is the result of other men and of the totality of human society and experience. I realize that I am putting this forward rather blandly, but it is all new to me; and newcomers tend to simplify and (as you would say, my dear sister) vulgarize a science of which they possess some small knowledge.

Yet my thinking was borne out to some degree during a very pleasant dinner I had with Miss Oland. It was not easy to get her to have dinner with me. You see, I don't think she liked me very much, although I am presuming to say that she likes me a little better now. But in the beginning, her attitude was very much shaped by my objective and somewhat cold and investigative attitude toward what had happened to the little boy.

Miss Oland, may I say, is a very intelligent young lady, an attractive young lady, and a very devout Quaker. She takes her religion with great seriousness, and she lives it. It was a nice and perhaps constructive blow to my ego to realize that she looked down upon me with a mixture of dislike and pity. I think, however, that Miss Oland and people like her look down upon most of the human race. I put this surmise of mine to her, and she denied it very hotly. In fact, she was so annoyed by the thought that I wonder whether she will agree to spend another evening with me.

However, there is no doubt in my mind but that people like Miss Oland occupy the role of the outsider. They watch the human race, without actually belonging to it. I have noticed this same attitude in a number of well-educated Jews I have met. But Miss Oland is the first Quaker with whom I ever discussed these things. I would hardly be surprised if her attitude were shared by other Quakers of sensitivity and thoughtfulness.

Miss Oland regards me as a barbarian—less a barbarian, of course, than such an obvious creature as the white hunter Ned Archway. But only by contrast with him do I become admirable, and at that only slightly admirable. As Miss Oland put it to me:

"You profess your superiority to the white hunter, Mr. Felton, and you look down on him as a rather uncivilized sort of man, but for what actually do you condemn him? For shooting the baboons for the fun of it or for beating the child?"

"For both," I replied.

"But he kills only animals, and surely the child will recover from the beating."

"And do you see virtue in killing animals for fun, as you put it?" I asked her.

"No virtue indeed, Mr. Felton, but I see less evil in it than in the slaughter of human beings."

"By that, just what do you mean, Miss Oland?"

"I mean that, like Ned Archway, you have been a hunter. You hunted men."

"What do you mean, I hunted men?"

"You told me you were an infantry captain, didn't you? What other purpose would an infantry captain have but the hunting down and the slaughter of human beings?"

"But that was different."

"How was it different, Mr. Felton?"

"My goodness, I don't have to go into all that, do I? You're not going to trap me with that old, old saw? You lived in the world that Adolf Hitler was remaking. You inhabited the same world that contained the concentration camps, the abattoirs, the gas ovens, the slaughter pits. How can you ask me such an absurd question?"

"Of course the question is absurd," she nodded. "Any question, Mr. Felton, becomes absurd when it is new to you or irritating to you or outside of your particular sphere of mental agreement. My question disturbed you; therefore, it becomes absurd."

"But surely you are not going to defend the Nazis."

"Now that indeed becomes rather absurd, doesn't it, Mr. Felton? You know that I would not defend the Nazis. How could you conceivably think that under any circumstances I would?"

"You're right. I could not conceivably think that. I admit it."

"I am not objecting, Mr. Felton, to your attitude toward the Nazis. I am simply objecting to your attitude toward killing. Obviously, you resent the pointless and

witless killing of baboons, but you do not resent the equally
pointless and witless slaughter of human beings."

"I like to think, Miss Oland, that I was fighting for
the survival of human civilization and of human dignity,
and that whatever killing I was forced to do was neither
thoughtless nor witless."

"Oh come now, Mr. Felton, we are both a little too
old for that sort of thing, aren't we? Were you fighting
for man's dignity? And by what process did you know
that whatever German soldier you happened to kill was
not equally aware of what was demanded by man's dignity? What did you know of that soldier's life or of his
record? Did you know whether he opposed Hitler, if he
did not oppose Hitler, how he agreed with Hitler, or
whether he agreed or disagreed with Hitler? You knew
nothing of that; and certainly you knew enough of military
structure to know that, like yourself, he had no choice but
to face you and fight you."

"He could surrender," I said.

"Could he really, Mr. Felton? Now I am going to
ask you a question. Did you shoot first and ask questions
afterwards? Or did you ask questions first and shoot afterwards? I have never been on a battlefield, but I have a
good imagination, and I have read many stories about what
goes on on a battlefield. Could he have surrendered, Mr.
Felton?"

"No," I admitted, "you're quite right. In most cases
he couldn't have surrendered. There were cases where he
could and maybe he did, but in most cases he could not
have surrendered. Certainly, as an individual, he could not

have surrendered. So you are absolutely right there, and I will not argue it. Nevertheless, I also will not relinquish my belief that there was a virture in our cause in World War II, a virtue in what we fought for and what so many of us died for."

"Then why don't you say that there was virtue in what you killed for, Mr. Felton?"

"I don't like to put it that way because I have never regarded myself as a killer."

"But the plain and naked fact of the matter, Mr. Felton, is that you are a killer. You have killed human beings, haven't you?"

"I have," I admitted weakly.

"I am not trying to pin you down to something nasty, Mr. Felton. I am not trying to derogate you, please believe me. It is only that no man takes any action without some sort of justification. He would go out of his mind if he did, wouldn't he? You ask me to prefer you to Mr. Archway, but I find that very hard to do. Really, I know this hurts you and I know I am not being polite, but from my point of view you and Archway inhabit the same world."

"And you don't inhabit that world, Miss Oland?" I wanted to know.

"No, not really. I am a Quaker, Mr. Felton. I think that my culture, the culture of my family, the culture of my people, has been different for many generations. We live among you but not with you. Your world is not our world. It really isn't, Mr. Felton, and you might do well to think about that. You seem very seriously interested in what has happened to this poor child. Maybe thinking about what I have just said would give you some clue as to what happens when a human child must live in a baboon's world."

"And at the same time," I said to her, "you have your little triumph and the great, great satisfaction of righteousness."

She did not argue that point. "Yes," she said, "I suppose I am righteous, Mr. Felton. I wish I knew how to be otherwise, and perhaps in time I will learn. For the moment I am young enough to feel righteous and disgusted as well. You have no idea how frequently I am disgusted, Mr. Felton."

So, you see, I can fail her for politeness and score her very low as regards hospitality, she having been in Pretoria at least six months longer than I. At the same time, even though she is a woman I will not remember fondly, I have to admire her, and, in the last analysis, I have to admit that she was speaking the truth.

All of which leads me to ask some very pertinent questions, sister mine. The man raised by a wolf is no longer a man, and the man raised by the baboons is no longer a man, and this fate is inevitable, isn't it? No matter what the man is, you put him with the apes and he becomes an ape and never very much more than that. My head has been swimming with all sorts of notions, some of them not at all pleasant. My dear sister, what the hell are you and your husband up to? Isn't it time you broke down and told old Harry, or do you want me to pop off to Tibet and hold converse with the lamas? I am ready for anything; I will be surprised by nothing, and I am prepared to go anywhere at all to please you. But, preferably, hand me something that adds up to a positive sum and then put a few words of explanation with it.

Your nasty killer brother,
Harry.

Chapter Nine

BY AIRMAIL

Washington, D.C.
November 27, 1945

Mr. Harry Felton
Pretoria, Union of South Africa

Dear Harry:

You are a good and sweet brother, and quite sharp, too. You are also a dear. You are patient and understanding, and you have trotted around dutifully in a maze without trying to batter your way out.

Now it comes down to this, Harry: Mark and I want you to do a job for us which will enable you to go here and there across the face of the earth, and be paid for it, too. In order to convince you, and to have your full coöperation and your very considerable creative abilities as well, we must spill out the dark secrets of our work—which we have decided to do, considering that you are an upright and trustworthy character. But the mail, it would seem, is less trustworthy; and since we are working with the

Army, which has a constitutional dedication to top-secrecy and similar nonsense, the information goes to you via diplomatic pouch.

As of receiving this, that is, providing that you agree, you may consider yourself employed. Your expenses will be paid—travel, hotel and per diem—within reason, and there will be an additional eight thousand a year, less for work than for indulgence. In fact, as I write it down here, it makes so absolutely intriguing a proposition that I am tempted to throw over my own job and take yours instead.

So please stay put at your hotel in Pretoria until the diplomatic pouch arrives. I promise you that this will be in not more than ten days. They will certainly find you —that is, the diplomatic courier will.

Love, affection and respect,
Jean.

Chapter Ten

Washington, D.C.
December 5, 1945

Mr. Harry Felton
Pretoria, Union of South Africa

Dear Harry:

Consider this letter the joint effort of Mark and myself. The thinking is ours and the conclusions are also shared. Also, Harry, consider this to be a very serious document indeed.

You know that for the past twenty years we have both been deeply concerned with child psychology and child development. There is no need to review our careers or our experience in the Public Health Service. Our work during the war, as part of the Child Reclamation Program, led to an interesting theory, which we decided to pursue. We were given leave by the head of the service to make this our own project. The leave is a sort of five-year sabbatical, with the option given to us at the end of five years to extend the leave for five years more, and a third five years then, if necessary. Recently, we were granted a substantial amount of Army funds to work with. In return for this, we have agreed to put our findings at the disposal of the Government.

Now to get down to the theory, which is not entirely untested. As you know, Mark and I have behind us two decades of practical work with children. When I say practical, I cover a good deal of ground. Since we are both physicians, we have worked with children as pediatricians. We have done hospital work with children. We have operated on children as surgeons; and, under certain conditions (as, for example, during emergencies in the early years of the war), we have pioneered surgical work with children simply because we were placed in a position which left us no other choice. We have also tested children, observed children, and gathered thousands of pages of data pertaining to the intelligence of children. From this vast experience, we have come to some curious conclusions. I would put it better if I said that we have come to a great many conclusions, but have now focused our interest on one conclusion in particular, namely this: Mark and I have come to believe that within the rank and file of Homo sapiens is the beginning of a new race.

Call this new race "man-plus"—call it what you will. The people who constitute this new race of men are not of recent arrival; they have been cropping up among men —Homo sapiens, that is—for hundreds, perhaps for thousands, of years. But they are trapped in the human environment; they are trapped in the company of man, and they are molded by the company of man and by the human environment as certainly and as implacably as your wolf-girl was trapped among the wolves or your Bantu child among the baboons. So, you see, the process is quite certain.

Everything that you discovered in Assam and in South Africa tended to bear out our own conclusions. Just as the little Assamese girl was divested of her humanity, deprived of her membership in the human race, by being reared among the wolves, so is our theoretical man-plus deprived of his racehood, of his normal plus-humanity, by living among men. Perhaps your Bantu boy would be a closer parallel to what we mean. I will not at this point try to explain more fully. Later on in this letter we will go into other details of our theory; and, if you agree to work with us, as your work progresses, so will your understanding of exactly what we are after.

By the way, your two cases of animal child-rearing are not the only attested ones we have. By sworn witness, we have records of seven similar cases: one in Russia, two in Canada, two in South America, one in West Africa and, just to cut us down to size, one in the United States of America. This does not mean that all seven of these cases are wholly authenticated. If we were to turn to each in succession and apply to it the kind of severe interviewing and testing that you have applied to the two cases you investigated, we might find that of the seven cases perhaps all are fictional, perhaps one is based on reality, perhaps all are based on reality. We might come to any one of these conclusions. *A priori*, we are not able to do more than accept the facts and apply to these facts our own judgment.

You may add to this the hearsay and folklore of three hundred and eleven parallel cases which cover a period of fourteen centuries. We have in fifteenth-century Germany, in the folio manuscript of the monk Hubercus, five case histories he claims to have observed personally. In all of these cases, in the seven cases witnessed by people alive today, and in all but sixteen of the hearsay cases, the result is more or less precisely what you have seen and described yourself; that is, the child reared by the wolf is divested of humanity.

We have yet been unable to find a case, mythological or otherwise, in which the child reared by the wolf is able subsequently to learn man's speech. Mythology adds up to a little—of course, very little. But speaking in mythological terms, we can find over forty such cases that survived from great antiquity in the mythologies of one nation or another.

But of course, Harry, we are not attempting to prove that animals can rear a human child, or that human children have been so reared, or that any of the facts connected with human children so reared are true. We are merely attempting to use these cases of the rearing of human children by animals as indications of what may face superior-man reared by man. You see, our own work adds up to the parallel conclusion: the child reared by a man is a man. And what is a man? In the broadest historical sense, a man is a creature who builds social organizations, the major purpose of such organizations being man's own destruction.

The Trap

If what I have just written were an ethical or moral judgment, it could certainly be challenged and perhaps success-
fully; however, it is not by any means a judgment; it is
simply an historical conclusion. If one examines the history
of man with total objectivity, one can only come to the
conclusion that man's existence as a social being has been
mainly for the purpose of war. All that he has achieved,
all that he has built, has been achieved and has been built
in the intervals between wars, thereby creating a social
organism that can function during a war and in the act of
war. This is by no means a judgment, nor is it an historical
observation upon man as an individual. Man as an individual would have to be described quite differently. But
we must not for one moment forget that we have just come
through a holocaust that has consumed fifty million human
lives. I refer to World War II, in which we all played
our parts. We have now calculated that the toll of
human life internationally in World War II was above fifty
million men, women and children. This is larger than the
entire human population of the earth at the time of the
Roman Empire. We are used to large numbers today; it
puts a little different light on the figure when we observe
to ourselves that we have just succeeded in destroying in
a period of less than five years more human beings than
existed upon the entire face of the earth two thousand
years ago. That is one to think about, isn't it, Harry? But
the observation—the historical observation of the role of
man—is made here in a purely clinical sense and in terms
of man-plus.

You see, if man-plus exists, he is trapped and caged as

certainly as any human child reared by animals is caged. In the same way the incipient man-plus is divested of whatever his potential is. The wolf dealing with our little Assamese girl would hardly be able to calculate or even to guess what she might have been in her own civilization. The wolf can only see her as the product of a wolf society. If man-plus exists, we see him and we have always seen him as a product of man's society. Of course, we have no proof that he exists. We have simply created a supposition that he exists, and we have enough evidence at our disposal for us to support this proposition. This, of course, is a usual procedure among scientists. Einstein's conception of the shape of the universe and of the curvature of light was hypothetical to begin with; it originated as a creative idea. After he had formulated the hypothesis, he set about proving it in physical terms. And we shall follow a similar method.

Why do we think the super-child exists? Well, there are many reasons, and we have neither the time nor the space here to go into all of them, or into much detail. However, here are two very telling and important reasons:

Firstly, we have gathered together the case histories of several hundred men and women who as children had IQ's of 170 or above. Since these men and women are now adults, their testing goes back to the early days of the Binet-Simon method, and it is by no means reliable—that is if any intelligence testing, any system of IQ, is reliable. We do not operate on the presumption that IQ testing has any objective reliability; we simply use it as a gauge and in lieu of anything better. In spite of the enormous intellectual promise as children of these several hundred men and women, less than ten percent have succeeded in their chosen careers. Considering how small the whole group is, their record of disaster and tragedy deserves attention in itself.

Another ten percent, roughly speaking, have been institutionalized as mental cases beyond recovery—that is, as pathological cases on the path to disintegration. About fourteen percent of the group have had or now require therapy for mental health problems; in this fourteen percent, roughly half have been in psychoanalysis or are in psychoanalysis or some similar therapy. Nine percent of the group have been suicides. One percent are in prison. Twenty-seven percent have had one or more divorces, nineteen percent are chronic failures at whatever they attempt—and the rest are undistinguished in any important manner. That is to say, they have not achieved even nominal success in the lines of endeavor they finally chose to follow. All of the IQ's have dwindled—and the dwindling of these IQ's, when graphed, bears a relationship to age. About four percent of the group studied have gone under the hundred or normal mark and are now in the condition of social morons.

Since society has never provided the full potential for such a mentality—that is, a mentality such as this group seemed to have had as children—we are uncertain as to what this potential might be. We have no valid, provable reasons to imagine that this group or a similar group would achieve more under other conditions; but against that we have every reason of logic and common sense so to suppose. Our guess is that this group has been reduced to a sort of idiocy, an idiocy that puts them on the level with what we call normalcy. But having been put on that level, they could not become men any more than your Assamese child could become a wolf. Unable to live out their lives, unable to become men, they were simply divested of their destiny, biological and otherwise, and in that sense destroyed. So much for the first reason, Harry.

The second reason we put forward is this: we know that man uses only a tiny part of his brain. Extensive testing enables us to put this forward as a provable fact, but we have no idea what blocks the human ego from using the rest of the human brain. We have to ask why nature has given man equipment that he cannot put to use—not atrophied equipment such as the appendix, but equipment that marks or is definitive of the highest life form ever produced by evolution. We must ask why nature has done this. We must also ask whether society, human society, prevents human beings from breaking the barriers that surround their own potential. In other words, have human beings themselves created a cage which prevents them from ever being more than human beings?

There, in brief, are the two reasons I spoke about before. Believe me, Harry, there are many more—enough for us to have convinced some very hard-headed and unimaginative Government people that we deserve a chance to release super-men. Of course, history helps—in its own mean and degraded manner. It would appear that we are beginning another war, this time with Russia; a cold war, as some have already taken to calling it. Among other things, it will be a war of intelligence—a commodity in rather short supply these days, as some of our local mental giants have been frank enough to admit.

Our new breed of computer warriors licked their lips when we sounded them out. They can't wait to have at another blood bath with all their new gimmicks; they have fed their tapes into the machines, and they have come out with new and enticing methods of human destruction. They look upon our man-plus as a secret weapon, little devils who will come up with death rays and superatom-bombs and all sorts of similar benign devices when the time is ripe. Well, let them think that way. It is inconceivable to imagine a project like ours, a project so enormous and so expensive, under benign sponsorship. The important thing is that Mark and I have been placed in full charge of the venture—millions of dollars, top priority, the whole works. We are subject to no one; we must report to no one; we have complete independence. We can requisition what we wish within reason, and we have a long period of time—that is, five years with an extension of an additional five years, and the very real possibility of another extension after that.

But nevertheless, Harry, the project is secret. I cannot stress this enough. This secrecy is not simply the childish classification business that the Army goes into; we support them on the question of secrecy. It is as important to us as to the Army, and I simply cannot stress this sufficiently or make it sound more serious than it actually is.

Now, as to your own job—that is, if you want it. And somehow or other, at this point I cannot envision you saying No. The job will develop step by step, and it is up to you to make it. First step: in Berlin, in 1937, there was a Professor Hans Goldbaum. He was half Jewish. He lectured on child psychology at the university, and he was also the head of the Berlin Institute for Child Therapy. He published a small monograph on intelligence testing in children, and he put forward claims—which we are inclined to believe —that he could determine a child's IQ during its first year of life, in its pre-speech period. The use of the term "IQ" is mine, not his. Professor Goldbaum had no use for the intelligence-quotient system that was developed by the Binet-Simon people, and he rejected it entirely. Instead, he devised his own method of intelligence testing, a very interesting method indeed.

He presented some impressive tables of estimations and subsequent checked results; but we do not know enough of his method to practice it ourselves. In other words, we need the professor's help.

In 1937, Professor Goldbaum vanished from Berlin. All of our efforts, combined with the very generous investigatory help of Army Intelligence, have convinced us that he was not murdered by the Nazis but that in some manner he escaped from Berlin. In 1943, a Professor Hans Goldbaum, either the same man in whom we are interested or someone of the same name, was reported to be living in Cape Town. That is the last address we have for him, and I am enclosing the address herewith. Now, as for you, Harry, here goes your job. You should leave for Cape Town immediately. Somehow or other, find the Professor Goldbaum reported to be in Cape Town. Find out whether he is our Professor Goldbaum. If he is not there, but has left, then follow him. Follow him wherever he has gone. Find him. I am not telling you how and, in turn, I do not expect you to ask us how. It is up to you. Find him! Naturally, all expenses will be paid. Of course, he may be dead. If that is the case, inform us immediately.

At this point I am no longer asking whether or not you will take the job. Either you will take it or I cease to be your sister, and I will curse your name and strike it out of all the family journals, etc. We love you and we need your help; in fact, we need it desperately, and at this moment I know of no one else who could substitute for you.

Jean.

Chapter Eleven

BY AIRMAIL

Cape Town, South Africa
December 20, 1945

MRS. JEAN ARBALAID
WASHINGTON, D. C.

My dear Sister:

I could write a book about my week in Cape Town. This is a city I am not in love with, and if I get out of here alive I have no desire ever to return. The days have been very interesting indeed, as you will see, and the nights have been occupied with nightmares about your harebrained scheme for super-man. Instead of sleeping peacefully, I dream of rows of little devils preparing all sorts of hideous death rays for your Army partners. What are you up to? No, I am not quitting. I am not walking out. A job is a job, and I remain your faithful employee.

Let me tell you something about the professor. Evidently, in one way or another he was important to the Nazis—that is, important enough for them to desire to eliminate him. There was a very considerable organization of the Nazi bully boys here in Cape Town when the war began, and they had Herr Goldbaum on their list. A few days after he arrived, an attempt was made on his life. He received a superficial bullet wound, but it became infected and he had rather a bad time of it. The Jewish community took care of him and hid him, but then things got a little hot, and they turned him over to some friends they had in the Kaffir compound. I was following the trail, an old and stale trail, but one that became the path of duty and all that. Leave it to your brilliant brother Harry. I did not meet up with any revanchist Nazis who had survived the war and were hiding out for *der Tag*, whenever it might come. No, indeed. I simply followed this cold trail into the Kaffir compound, and thereby was picked up by the police and tossed into jail. They had me tagged for a Communist; can you imagine? I thought that just about everything had happened to me, but this was it. It took two days of argument and the efforts of the American Consul General as well, to prove that I was the very conservative and rather thoughtless brother of one of our most eminent Americans. I am a little tired of the weight your name carries, but thank heavens it carried enough weight to take me out of one of the most uncomfortable jails I have ever occupied or ever read about. It was crawling with bugs—huge, terrifying South African bugs.

After I got out of jail, I did the sensible thing that I should have done in the beginning. I sought an interview with the head of the Jewish community here, a Rabbi Anatole Bibberman. Bibberman, it seems, is an amateur

Assyriologist—and, if I do not make myself entirely plain, Assyriologists are a small group who devote their spare time to the study of ancient Assyria. I imagine a good many of them devote full time to the subject and become pros. Rabbi Bibberman, however, is a spare time Assyriologist; and it turns out that Professor Goldbaum shared his interest. They spent long hours, I am told, discussing ancient Assyria and Babylon and things of that sort.

The Rabbi told me something that he thought everyone knew—that is, everyone who is interested in Professor Goldbaum. He told me that in 1944 the people in London (and by people I suppose he meant scientists or physicians or something of that sort) discovered that Professor Goldbaum was holed up in Cape Town. They needed him for something or other, and he took off for London. I am leaving for London myself as soon as I finish this letter, and goodbye to Cape Town. As you plan my itinerary for the future, I would appreciate your eliminating Cape Town from the list.

Your ever-loving brother,
Harry.

Chapter Twelve

By *cable:*

MRS. JEAN ARBALAID
WASHINGTON, D.C.
DECEMBER 25, 1945

PERHAPS YOUR TRUST MISPLACED SINCE I
TAKE GLEEFUL AND CHILDISH PLEASURE IN
SENDING LONG LONG CABLES COLLECT
WHICH THE UNITED STATES ARMY PAYS FOR.
LIKE ANY OTHER MAN WHO HAS SERVED ANY
LENGTH OF TIME IN THIS HIDEOUS WAR WE
HAVE JUST FINISHED I SEEM TO HAVE AN
UNSHAKABLE BIAS AGAINST THE UNITED
STATES ARMY. BE THAT AS IT MAY I HAVE
FOUND THE PROFESSOR. IT WAS ABSURDLY
EASY AND IN A LETTER TO FOLLOW I WILL
GIVE ALL THE DETAILS. HE IS A CHARMING
AND DELIGHTFUL LITTLE MAN AND LAST

Howard Fast

NIGHT I TOOK HIM FOR A CHRISTMAS EVE DINNER TO SIMPSON'S. IT TURNED OUT THAT HE IS A VEGETARIAN. CAN YOU IMAGINE A VEGETARIAN AT SIMPSON'S ON CHRISTMAS EVE? I SUPPOSE AT THIS POINT I SHOULD PUT IN A STOP JUST TO INDICATE THAT I AM QUITE AWARE THAT I AM SENDING YOU A CABLE BUT I HAVE HEARD IT TOLD ON RELIABLE AUTHORITY THAT THE NEW YORK TIMES REPORTERS CABLE THOSE ENDLESS STORIES OF THEIRS IN FULL AND NOT IN CABLESE SO I PRESUME ON THIS TIDBIT. MAY I SAY THAT THE PROFESSOR IS IN-TRIGUED BY THE LITTLE I HAVE TOLD HIM. I DID NOT KNOW HOW MUCH TO TELL HIM OR HOW HARD TO PUSH. JUST WHAT DO YOU WANT ME TO DO WITH HIM? WHAT SHALL I ASK HIM? WHAT SHALL I TELL HIM? YOU CAN SEE THAT SINCE THIS IS A PUBLIC CABLE I AM USING GUARDED CIR-CUITOUS AND SOMETIMES RATHER SILLY LANGUAGE. I TRUST YOU UNDERSTAND ME MY DEAR JEAN. WHAT NOW?

HARRY FELTON.

(132

Chapter Thirteen

BY DIPLOMATIC POUCH

Washington, D. C.
December 26, 1945

MR. HARRY FELTON
LONDON, ENGLAND

Dear Harry:

While I am delighted that your spell of depression has disappeared, you are beginning to worry me just a wee bit with your silliness. I try to remember whether you were always as light-headed as you now appear to be, and I keep telling myself and Mark that the war has changed you. In any case, you are our man on the spot, and we must go along with you. The truth is, I'm teasing. We do trust you, dear, but please be more serious. Our project is dead serious. We believe that despite protestations of your own limitations, you have enough sense and good instincts to gauge Professor Goldbaum's method. Talk to him. Unless you believe he is a complete fraud—and from the little you say, I doubt that--we want you to sell him on this

venture. Sell him! We will give him whatever he asks—
that is, in the way of financial remuneration. A man like
Professor Goldbaum, according to all my past experience
with such men, should be more or less indifferent to
money; but even if he is, Harry, I want you to set his fee
and to set it generously. We want to make an arrangement
whereby he will continue to work with us for as long as
we need him. If it must be less than that, try to specify some
contractual terms, at least a year. As far as his future is
concerned, I repeat that we are able to take care of his
future; we will take care of it financially, and we will take
care of it in terms of citizenship. If he desires American
citizenship, we can arrange that with no trouble whatsoever. If he wishes to continue as a British national—I presume that is his status now—then we will smooth the way.
No difficulty will be encountered.

I am sure that when you discuss the matter with him
he will have a number of questions of his own, and he will
desire to be enlightened more fully than we have enlightened you. Perhaps we should have briefed you more
completely before now; but the truth of the matter is that
we had not yet completed our own preparations, nor were
we exactly decided on what our procedure would be. At
this point we are.

We have been allocated a tract of eight thousand
acres in northern California. The eight thousand acres are
very attractive. There is a stand of sequoia forest, a lovely
lake, and some very beautiful and arable meadowland. There
is also a stretch of badland. All in all, it is a variegated
and interesting landscape. Here we intend to establish an

environment. which will be under military guard and under military security. In other words, we propose to make this environment as close to a self-contained world as perhaps ever existed. In the beginning, in the first years of our experiment, the outside world will be entirely excluded. The environment will be exclusive and it will be controlled as absolutely as anything can be controlled within the present world and national situation.

Within this environment, we intend to bring forty children to maturity—to a maturity that will result in man-plus. But please understand, Harry, and convey this to the professor, that when I state something as a positive I am proceeding on a theoretical hypothesis. Man-plus does not exist and may never exist. We are making an experiment based on a presumption. Always come back to that, Harry; never talk as if we were dealing with certainties.

As to the details of the environment—well, most of it will have to wait. I can tell you this: We shall base its functioning on the highest and the gentlest conclusions of man's philosophy through the ages. There is no way to put this into a few sentences. Perhaps I might say that instead of doing unto others as we would have them do unto us, we will attempt to do not unto others as we would not have them do unto us. Of course that says everything and anything, and perhaps nothing as well; but in due time we will tell you the details of the environment as we plan it, and the details of its functioning. The more immediate and important problem is finding the children. We need a certain type of child—that is, a superior child, a very superior child. We would like to have the most extraordinary geniuses in all the world; but, since these children are to be very young, our success in that direction must always be open to question. But we are going to try.

As I said, we intend to raise forty children. Out of these forty children, we hope to find ten in the United States of America; the other thirty will be found by the professor and yourself—outside of the United States.

Half are to be boys. We want an even boy-girl balance, and the reasons for that, I think, are quite obvious. All of the children are to be between the ages of six months and nine months, and all are to show indications of an exceedingly high IQ. As I said before, we would like to have extraordinary geniuses. Now, you may ask me how, how is this location of infant genius going to work? Well, Harry, there's where the professor comes into the picture, as your guide and mentor. How we are going to accomplish the problem at home, we have not fully worked out. But we believe that we have some methods, some hints, some directions that will ultimately lead us to success. In your case, we are depending upon the professor's method —that is, if his method is any good at all. If it is not—well, there are a dozen points where we can fail, aside from his methods.

We want five racial groupings: Caucasian, Indian, Chinese, Malayan and Bantu. Of course, we are sensible of the vagueness of these groupings, and you will have to have some latitude within them. As you know, racial definitions are at worst political and at best extremely imprecise. If you should find, let us say, three or four or five Bantu children who impress you as extraordinary, naturally we want to include them. Again, when we say Bantu we are not being literal. You may find in South Africa a Hottentot child who commands your attention. By all means include the Hottentot child.

The six so-called Caucasian infants are to be found in Europe. We might suggest two Northern types, two Central European types and two Mediterranean types; but this is only a suggestion and by no means a blueprint for you to follow. Let me be more specific: If you should by any chance find seven children in Italy, all of whom are obviously important for our experiment, you must take all seven children, even though only six children are suggested from Europe.

Now the word "take" which I have just used—understand this: no cops and robbers stuff, no OSS tactics, no kidnapping. If you find the most marvelous, the most extraordinary, infant of your entire search, and the parents of that infant will not part with it, that ends the matter right there. This is not simply an ethical point that I am raising, Harry. This is integral to the success of our program, and I think that in time you will understand why.

Now, where will the children come from? We are going to buy children. Let us be brutally frank about it. We are in the market for children. Where will they come from? Unfortunately for mankind but perhaps fortunately for our narrow purpose here, the world abounds in war orphans—and also in parents so poor, so desperate, that they will sell their children if the opportunity arises. When you find a child in such a situation and you want the child and the parents are willing, you are to buy. The price is no object. Of course, I must add here that you should exercise a certain amount of common sense. When I say price is no object, I mean that if you have to pay a hundred thousand or a hundred and fifty thousand dollars for a child, you are to pay the price. If, on the other hand, a price is in the neighborhood of a million dollars, you are to think it over very carefully. This is not to say that we will not pay as high as a million dollars if the necessity arises; but at that price, I want you to be very certain of what you are doing. We have enormous backing and an enormous amount of money to work with; but regardless of how enormous our resources are at this moment, they are going to be spent eventually, and there are limitations. I am afraid that we must work within these limitations.

However, I will have no maudlin sentimentality or scruples about acquiring the children, and I would like you and the professor to share my point of view. We are scientists, and sentimentalism rarely advances science; also, in itself, I find sentimentalism a rather dreadful thing. Let me state emphatically that these children will be loved and cherished as much as it is possible for those who are not blood parents to love and cherish children; and in the case of these children that you acquire by purchase, you will be buying not only a child but, for that child, a life of hope and promise. Indeed, we hope to offer these children the most wonderful life that any child could have.

When you find a child that you want and you are ready to acquire that child, inform us immediately. Air transport will be at your disposal. We are also making all arrangements for wet nurses—that is to say, if you find a nursing infant who should continue to nurse, we will always have wet nurses available. Rest assured that all other details of child care will be anticipated. We will have a staff of excellent pediatricians whom you can call on any-where on earth. They will fly to where you are.

On the other hand, we do not anticipate a need for physicians. Above all things, we want healthy children, of course within the general conditions of health in any given area. We know that an extraordinary child in certain regions of the earth may well have the most discouraging signs of poor health, undernourishment, etc. But I am sure that you and Professor Goldbaum will be able to measure and assess such cases.

Good luck to you. We are depending on you, and we love you. We do wish that you could have been here with us for Christmas Day; but, in any case, a Merry Christmas to you, and may the future bring peace on earth and good will to all men.

Your loving sister,

Jean.

Chapter Fourteen

Copenhagen, Denmark
February 4, 1946

Mrs. Jean Arbalaid
Washington, D. C.

Dear Jean:

I seem to have caught your top-secret and classified disease, or perhaps I have become convinced that this is a matter wanting some kind of secrecy. That seems hard to believe in such a down-to-earth, practical and lovely place as Copenhagen. We have been here for three days now, and I am absolutely charmed by the city and delighted with the Danes. I set aside today, in any case a good part of today, to sum up my various adventures and to pass on to you whatever conclusions and opinions might be of some profit to you.

From my cables, you will have deduced that the professor and I have been doing a Cook's Tour of the baby market. My dear sister, this kind of shopping spree does not sit at all well with me; however, I gave my word, and there you are. I will complete and deliver. I might add that I have also become engrossed with your plans, and I doubt that I would allow myself to be replaced under any circumstances.

By the way, I suppose I continue to send these along to Washington, even though your "environment," as you call it, has been established? I will keep on doing so until otherwise instructed.

As you know, there was no great difficulty in finding the professor. Not only was he in the telephone book, but he is quite famous in London. He has been working for almost a year now with a child reclamation project, while living among the ruins of the East End, which was pretty badly shattered and is being reclaimed only slowly. He is an astonishing little man, and I have become fond of him. On his part, he is learning to tolerate me.

I think I cabled to you how I took him to dinner at Simpson's only to learn that he was a vegetarian. But did I say that you were the lever that moved him, my dear sister? I had no idea how famous you are in certain circles. Professor Goldbaum regarded me with awe, simply because you and I share a mother and a father. On the other hand, my respect for unostentatious scientific folk is growing. The second meeting I had with Dr. Goldbaum took place on the terrace of the House of Commons. This little fellow, who would be lost so easily in any crowd, had casually invited three Members of Parliament and one of His Majesty's Ministers to lunch with us. The subject under discussion was children: the future of children, the care of children, the love of children and the importance of children.

Whatever you may say about the Government here, its interest in the next generation is honest, moving, and very deep and real. For the first time in British history, the average Englishman is getting a substantial, adequate and balanced diet. They have wonderful plans and great excitement about the future and about children's role in the future. I think it was for this purpose, (to hear some of the plans) that Goldbaum invited me to be there. I am not sure that he trusts me—I don't mean this in a personal sense, but rather that I, being simply what I am, and he, being a sensitive man who recognizes what I am—well, why should he trust me? In that sense, he is quite right not to trust me.

At this lunch he drew me into the conversation, explaining to the others that I was deeply interested in children. They raised their eyebrows and inquired politely just where my interest derived from and where it was directed.

Believe me, my only claim to a decent standing in the human race was the fact that I was Mrs. Jean Arbalaid's brother; and when they heard that I was your brother their whole attitude toward me changed. I passed myself off as a sort of amateur child psychologist, working for you and assisting you, which is true in a way, isn't it? They were all very polite to me, and none of them questioned me too closely.

It was a good day, one of those astonishing blue-sky days that are real harbingers of spring, and that come only rarely in London in February. After the luncheon, the professor and I strolled along Bird Cage Walk, and then

through Saint James's Park to the Mall. We were both re-
laxed, and the professor's uncertainty about me was finally
beginning to crumble just a little. So I said my piece, all of
it, no holds barred. To be truthful, I had expected your
reputation to crumble into dust there on the spot, but no
such thing. Goldbaum listened with his mouth and his ears
and every fiber of his being. The only time he interrupted
me was to question me about the Assamese girl and the Bantu
boy; and very pointed and meticulous questions they were.

"Did you yourself examine the child?" he asked me.

"Not as a doctor," I replied, "but I did examine her
in the sense that one human being can observe another human being. This was not a calm little girl, nor was the Bantu
boy a calm little boy; they were both terror-stricken animals."

"Not animals," Goldbaum corrected me.

"No, of course not."

"You see," Goldbaum said, "that point is most important. Animals they could not become; they were prevented,
however, from becoming human beings."

There he hit upon the precise point that I had come
to and which Professor Gojee had underlined so often.
When I had finished with my whole story, and had, so to
speak, opened all my cards to Professor Goldbaum's inspection, he simply shook his head—not in disagreement, but
with sheer excitement and wordless delight. I then asked
him what his reaction to all this was.

"I need time," he said. "This is something to digest.
But the concept, Mr. Felton, is wonderful—daring and wonderful. Not that the reasoning behind it is so novel. I have

thought of this same thing; so many anthropologists have thought of it. Also, throughout the ages it has been a concept in many philosophies. The Greeks gave their attention to it, and many other ancient peoples speculated upon it. But always as an imaginative concept, as a speculation, as a sort of beautiful daydream. To put it into practice, young man—ah, your sister is a wonderful and a remarkable woman!"

There you are, my sister. I struck while the iron was hot, and told him then and there that you wanted and needed his help, first to find the children and then to work in the environment.

"The environment," he said. "You understand, that is everything, everything. But how can she change the environment? The environment is total, the whole fabric of human society, self-deluded and superstitious and sick and irrational and clinging to the legends and the fantasies and the ghosts. Who can change that?"

I had my answer ready, and I told him that if anyone could, Mrs. Jean Arbalaid could.

"You have a great deal of respect for your sister," he said. "I am told that she is a very gentle woman."

"When she is not crossed," I agreed. "But the point is this, Professor: Will you work with us? That is the question she wants me to put to you."

"But how can I answer it now? You confront me with perhaps the most exciting, the most earth-shaking notion in all of human history—not as a philosophical notion but as a pragmatic experiment—and then you ask me to say Yes or No. Impossible!"

"All right," I agreed, "I can accept that. How long do you want to think about it?"

"Overnight will be enough," he said. "Now tell me about California. I have never been there. I have read a little about it. Tell me what the state is like and what sort of an environment this would be in a physical sense; I would also like to know something more specific about your sister's relations to what you call 'the Army.' That phrase you use, 'the Army'—it seems quite different from what we understand in European terms or even in British terms."

So it went. My anthropology is passable at best, but I have read all your books. My geography and history are better, and if my answers were weak where your field was concerned, he did manage to draw out of me a more or less complete picture of Mark and yourself, and as much sociological and political information concerning the United States Government, the United States Army, and the relationship of the Government and the Army to subprojects, as I could have provided under any circumstances. He has a remarkable gift for extracting information, or, as I am inclined to regard it, of squeezing water from a rock.

When I left him, he said that he would think the whole matter over. We made an appointment for the following day. Then, he said, provided he had agreed to join us, he would begin to instruct me in his method of determining the intelligence of infants.

By the way, just to touch on his methods, he makes a great point of the fact that he does not test but rather determines, leaving himself a wide margin for error. Years before, in prewar Germany, he had worked out a list of about fifty characteristics which he had noted in infants. All of these characteristics had some relationship to factors of intelligence and response. As the infants in whom he had originally noted these characteristics matured, they were tested regularly by standard methods, and the results of these tests were compared with his original observations. Thereby he began to draw certain conclusions, which he tested again and again during the next fifteen years. Out of these conclusions and out of his tests, his checking, his relating testing to observation, he began to put together a list of characteristics that the pre-tested (that is, the new) infant might demonstrate, and he specified how those characteristics could be relied upon to indicate intelligence. Actually, his method is as brilliant as it is simple, and I am enclosing here an unpublished article of his which goes into far greater detail. Suffice it to say he convinced me of the validity of his methods.

I must note that subsequently, watching him examine a hundred and four British infants and watching him come up with our first choice for the group, I began to realize how brilliant this man is. Believe me, Jean, he is a most remarkable and wise man, and anything and everything you may have heard about his talents and knowledge is less than the reality.

When I met him the following day, he agreed to join the project. Having come to this conclusion, he had no reservations about it. He seemed to understand the consequences far better than I did, and he told me very gravely just what his joining meant. Afterwards I wrote it down exactly as he said it:

"You must tell your sister that I have not come to this decision lightly. We are tampering with human souls—and perhaps even with human destiny. This experiment may fail, but if it succeeds it can be the most important event of our time—even more important and consequential than this terrible war we have just been through. And you must tell her something else. I once had a wife and three children, and they were put to death because a nation of men had turned into beasts. I personally lived through and observed that transition, that unbelievable and monstrous mass transition of men into beasts—but I could not have lived through it unless I had believed, always, that what can turn into a beast can also turn into a human being. We—and by we I mean the present population of the earth—are neither beast nor man. When I speak the word 'man,' I speak it proudly. It is a goal, not a fact. It is a dream, not a reality. Man does not exist. We are professing to believe that he might exist. But if we go ahead to create man, we must be humble. We are the tool, not the creator, and if we succeed, we ourselves will be far less than the result of our work. You must also tell your sister that when I make this commitment as I do today, it is a commitment without limitation. I am no longer a young man, and if this experiment is to be pursued properly, it must take up most, perhaps the rest, of my life. I do not lightly turn over the rest of my existence to her—and yet I do."

There is your man, Jean, and as I said, very much of a man. The words above are quoted verbatim. He also dwells a great deal on the question of environment, and the wisdom and judgment and love necessary to create this environment. He understands, of course, that in our work—in our attempt to find the children to begin the experiment with—we are relying most heavily upon heredity. He does not negate the factor of heredity by any means, but heredity without the environment, he always underlines, is useless. I think it would be helpful if you could send me a little more information about this environment that you are establishing. Perhaps Professor Goldbaum could make a contribution toward it while it is in the process of being created.

We have now sent you four infants. Tomorrow we leave for Rome, and from Rome for Casablanca. We will be in Rome for at least two weeks and you can write or cable me there. The Embassy in Rome will have our whereabouts at any time.

More seriously than ever and not untroubled.

Harry.

Chapter Fifteen

BY DIPLOMATIC POUCH

Via Washington, D. C.
February 11, 1946

Mr. Harry Felton
Rome, Italy

Dear Harry:

Just a few facts here—not nearly as many as we would like to give you concerning the environment, but at least enough for Professor Goldbaum to begin to orient himself. We are tremendously impressed by your reactions to Professor Goldbaum, and we look forward eagerly to his completing his work in Europe and joining us as a staff member here in America. By the way, he is the only staff member, as such, that we will have. Later on in this letter, I will make that clear. Meanwhile, Mark and I have been working night and day on the environment. In the most general terms, this is what we hope to accomplish and to have ready for the education of the children:

Howard Fast

The entire reservation—all eight thousand acres—will be surrounded by a wire fence, what is commonly known as heavy tennis fencing or playground fencing. The fence will be eleven feet high; it will be topped by a wire carrying live current, and it will be under Army guard twenty-four hours a day. However, the Army guards will be stationed a minimum of three hundred yards from the fence. They will be under orders never, at any time under any circumstances, to approach the main fence nearer than three hundred yards. Outside of this neutral strip of three hundred yards, a second fence will be built—what might be thought of as an ordinary California cow fence. The Army guards will patrol outside of this fence, and only under specific and special circumstances will they have permission to step within it into the neutralized zone. In this way, and through the adroit use of vegetation, we hope that, for the first ten years at least, people within the reservation will neither see nor have any other indication of the fact that outside of the reservation an armed guard patrols and protects it.

Within the reservation itself we shall establish a home; indeed, the most complete home imaginable. Not only shall we have living quarters, teaching quarters, and the means of any and all entertainment we may require; but we shall also have machine shops, masonry shops, wood-carving shops, mills, all kinds of fabrication devices and plans—in other words, almost everything necessary for absolute independence and self-maintenance. This does not mean that we are going to cut our relationships with the outside. There will certainly be a constant flow of material from the outside into the environment, for we shall require many things that we shall not be able to produce ourselves.

Now for the population of the environment: We expect to enlist between thirty and forty teachers or group parents. We are accepting only young married couples who love children and who will dedicate themselves entirely to this venture. This in itself has become a monumental task, for enlistment in this project is even more of a commitment than enlistment in the Army was five years ago. We are telling those parents who accept our invitation and who are ready to throw in their lot with the experiment that the minimum time they will be asked to spend with us is fifteen years, and that the maximum time may well be a lifetime. In other words, the people who accept our invitation and come with us to be a part of the environment are, in actuality, leaving the planet Earth. They are leaving their friends and they are leaving their relatives, not for a day, a week, a month, or a year, but in a manner of speaking, forever. It is as if you were to approach twenty married couples and suggest to them that they emigrate from Earth to an uninhabited planet with no possibility of a return.

Can you imagine what this is, Harry? Can you imagine how keenly these people must believe? You might well suppose that nowhere could we find people who would be willing to join us in our venture; but that is far from the case. It is true that we are going all over the world for the parents, just as we are going all over the world for the children. However, we have already enlisted twelve couples, superb people, of several nationalities. We are excited and delighted with every step forward we take. Remember, it is not enough to find couples willing to dedicate themselves to this venture; they must have unique additional qualifications; and the fact that we have found so many with these qualifications is what excites us and gives us faith in the possibility that we will succeed.

To even begin this experiment, we must dedicate ourselves to the proposition that somewhere in man's so-called civilized development, something went tragically wrong; therefore, we are returning to a number of forms of great antiquity. One of these forms is group marriage. That is not to say that we will cohabit indiscriminately; rather, the children will be given to understand that parentage is a whole, a matter of the group—that we are all their mothers and their fathers, not by blood but by a common love, a common feeling for protection and a common feeling for instruction.

As far as teaching is concerned, we shall teach our children only the truth. Where we do not know the truth, we shall not teach. There will be no myths, no legends, no lies, no superstitions, no false premises and no religions. There will be no gods, no bogeymen, no horrors, no nameless fears. We shall teach love and compassion and coöperation; and with this we shall demonstrate, in our lives and in every action we take, the same love and compassion—hoping, trusting and fighting for all of this to add up to the fullest possible measure of security. We shall also teach them the knowledge of mankind—but not until they are ready for that knowledge, not until they are capable of handling it. Certainly we shall not give them knowledge of the history of mankind or what mankind has become in the course of that history until after they have completed the first eight years of their lives. Thus they will grow up knowing nothing of war, knowing nothing of murder, knowing nothing of the thing called patriotism, unaware of the multitude of hatreds, of fears, of hostilities that has become the common heritage of all of mankind.

During the first nine years in the environment, we shall have total control. We have already installed a complete printing press, a photo-offset system; we have all the moving-picture equipment necessary, and we have laboratories to develop the film we take, projection booths and theaters. All the film we need we shall make. We shall write the books; we shall take the film; we shall shape the history as history is taught to them in the beginning—that is, a history of who they are and what they are within the environment. We shall raise them in a sort of Utopia—God willing, without all the tragic mistakes that man has always made in his Utopias. And, finally, when we have produced something strong and healthy and beautiful and sturdy—at that point only will we begin to relate the children to the world as it is. Does it sound too simple or presumptuous? I am almost sorry, Harry, that I cannot make it more complicated, more intriguing, more wonderful, yet Mark and I both agree that the essence of what we are attempting to do is simple beyond belief; it is almost negative. We are attempting to rid ourselves of something that mankind has done to itself; and, if we can rid a group of children of that undefined something, then what will emerge just might be exciting and wonderful and even magnificent beyond belief. That is our hope; but the environment as I describe it above,

Harry, is all that we can do—and I think that Professor Goldbaum will understand that full well and will not ask more of us. It is also a great deal more than has ever been done for any children on this earth heretofore.

So good luck to both of you. May you work well and happily and complete your work. The moment it is completed we want Professor Goldbaum to join us in the United States and to become a part of our group and our experiment. I am not asking you to become a part of it, Harry, and I think you understand why. I don't want to put you in a position of having to make the choice. By now I can well understand how deeply you have committed yourself to our experiment. Mark and I both realize that you cannot spell out such a commitment, but, dear Harry, I know you so well and I know what has happened inside of you. If I asked you to join us, you would not allow yourself to say No; but, at the same time, I don't think that your road to happiness consists of taking off for another planet. However you might feel about it, Harry, you are far too attached to the reality of the world as it is. You have not yet found the woman that you must find, but when you do find her, Harry, she and you will have your own way to find.

Your letters, in spite of your attempt to make them highly impersonal, do give us a clue to the change within you. Do you know, Harry, everyone associated with this experiment begins a process of change—and we feel that same curious process of change taking place within us.

When I put down simply and directly on paper what we are doing now and what we intend to do in the future, it seems almost too obvious to be meaningful in any manner.

The Trap

In fact, when you look at it again and again, it seems almost ridiculously simple and pointless and hopeless. What are we doing, Harry? We are simply taking a group of very gifted children and giving them knowledge and love. Is this enough to break through to that part of man which is unused and unknown? We don't know, Harry, but in time we shall see. Bring us the children, Harry, and we shall see.

With love,
Jean.

Chapter Sixteen

One day in the early spring of 1965, Harry Felton arrived in Washington from London. At the airport he took a cab directly to the White House, where he was expected.

Felton had just turned fifty; he was a tall and pleasant-looking man, rather lean, with graying hair. As president of the board of Shipways, Inc.—one of the country's largest import and export houses, with offices in London and in New York—Felton commanded a certain amount of deference and respect from Eggerton, who was then Secretary of Defense. A cold, withdrawn, and largely unloved man, Eggerton frequently adopted an attitude of immediate superiority, or, if that failed to impress, of judicious and controlled hostility; but he was sufficiently alert and sensitive not to make the mistake of trying to intimidate Felton.

Instead, he greeted him rather pleasantly—that is, pleasantly for Eggerton. The two of them, with no others present, sat down to talk in a small room in the White House. Drinks were served and a tray of sandwiches was brought in case Felton was hungry. Felton was not hungry. He and Eggerton drank each other's good health, and then they began to talk.

Eggerton proposed that Felton might know why he had been asked to Washington.

"I can't say that I do know," Felton replied—a little less than truthfully; but then, Felton did not like Eggerton and did not feel comfortable with him.

"You have a remarkable sister."

"I have been aware of that for a long time."

Felton seemed to take a moment to think about what he had just said, and then he smiled. Whatever made him smile was not revealed to Eggerton who, after a moment, asked him whether he felt that his statement had been humorous.

"No, I didn't feel that," Felton said seriously.

"You are being very careful here, Mr. Felton," the Secretary observed, "but you have trained yourself to be a very close-mouthed person. So far as we are able to ascertain, not even your immediate family has ever heard of manplus. That's a commendable trait."

"Possibly and possibly not. It's been a long time," Felton said coldly. "Just what do you mean by 'ascertain'? How have you been able to ascertain whether or not I am close-mouthed? That interests me, Mr. Secretary."

"Please don't be naïve, Mr. Felton."

"I have practiced being naïve for a lifetime," Felton said. "It's really not very sensitive on your part to ask me to change in a moment sitting here in front of you. I find that a degree of naïveté fits well with close-mouthedness. What did it come to, Mr. Secretary? Was my mail examined?"

"Now and then," the Secretary admitted.

"My offices bugged?"

"At times."

"And my home?"

"There have been reasons to keep you under observation, Mr. Felton. We do what is necessary. What we do has received large and unnecessary publicity; so I see no point in your claiming ignorance."

"I am sure you do what is necessary."

"We must, and I hope that this will not interfere with our little conversation today."

"It doesn't surprise me. So, in that direction at least, it will not interfere. But just what is this conversation and what are we to talk about?"

"Your sister."

"I see, my sister," Felton nodded. He did not appear surprised.

"Have you heard from your sister lately, Mr. Felton?"

"No, not for almost a year."

"Does it alarm you, Mr. Felton?"

"Does what alarm me?"

"The fact that you have not heard from your sister in so long?"

"Should it alarm me? No, it doesn't alarm me. My

161)

sister and I are very close, but this project of hers is not the sort of thing that allows for frequent social relations. Add to that the fact that my residence is in England, and that, while I do make trips to America, most of my time is spent in London and Paris. There have been long periods before when I have not heard from my sister. We are indifferent letter writers."

"I see," Eggerton said.

"Then I am to conclude that my sister is the reason for my visit here?"

"Yes."

"She is well?"

"As far as we know," Eggerton replied quietly.

"Then what can I do for you?"

"Help us if you will," Eggerton said just as quietly. He was visibly controlling himself—as if he had practiced with himself before the meeting and had conditioned himself not to lose his temper under any circumstances, but to remain quietly controlled, aloof and polite. "I am going to tell you what has happened, Mr. Felton, and then perhaps you can help us."

"Perhaps," Felton agreed. "You must understand, Mr. Eggerton, that I don't admire either your methods or your apparent goal. I think you would be wrong to look upon me as an ally. I spent the first twenty-four years of my life in the United States. Since then I have lived abroad with only infrequent visits here. So, you see, I am not even conditioned by what you might think of as a patriotic frame of mind. I am afraid that, if anything, I am a total internationalist."

"That doesn't surprise me, Mr. Felton."

"On second thought, I realize that it wouldn't. I am
sure that you have investigated my residences, my frame of
mind, my philosophy, and I would also guess that you have
enough recordings of my conversations with my most intimate friends to know exactly what my point of view is."

The Secretary of Defense smiled as if to exhibit to
Felton the fact that he, the Secretary of Defense, possessed
a sense of humor. "No, not quite that much, Mr. Felton,
but I must say that I am rather pleased by the respect you
have for our methods. It is true that we know a good deal
about you and it is also true that we could anticipate your
point of view. However, we are not calling upon you in
what some might term a patriotic capacity; we are calling
upon you because we feel that we can appeal to certain instincts which are very important to you."

"Such as?"

"Human beings, human decency, the protection of
mankind, the future of mankind—subjects that cross national
boundaries. You would agree that they do, would you not,
Mr. Felton?"

"I would agree that they do," Felton said.

"All right then; let us turn to your sister's project, a
project which has been under way so many years now. I
don't have to be hush-hush about it, because I am sure that
you know as much concerning this project as any of us—
more perhaps, since you were in at its inception. At that
time, you were on the payroll of the project, and for a number of months you assisted your sister in the beginnings of
the project. If I am not mistaken, part of your mission was

to acquire certain infants which she needed at that stage of her experiment?"

"The way you say 'infants,'" Felton replied, smiling, "raises a suspicion that we wanted them to roast and devour. May I assure you that such was not the case. We were neither kidnappers nor cannibals; our motives were rather pure."

"I am sure."

"You don't say it as if you were sure at all."

"Then perhaps I have some doubts, and perhaps you will share my doubts, Mr. Felton, when you have heard me out. What I intended to say was that surely you, of all people, realize that such a project as your sister undertook must be regarded very seriously indeed or else laughed off entirely. To date it has cost the Government of the United States upwards of one hundred and fourteen million dollars, and that is not something you laugh off, Mr. Felton."

"I had no idea the price was so high," Felton said. "On the other hand, you may have gotten a hundred and fourteen million dollars worth for your money."

"That remains to be seen. You understand, of course, that the unique part of your sister's project was its exclusiveness. That word is used advisedly and specifically. Your sister made the point again and again and again—and continues to make it, I may say—the point that the success of the project depended entirely upon its exclusiveness, upon the creation of a unique and exclusive environment. We were forced to accept her position and her demands—that is, if we desired the project at all; and it seems that the people who undertook to back the project did desire it. I say we,

Mr. Felton, because 'we' is a term we use in government; but you must understand that that was a good many years ago, almost twenty years ago, and I myself, Mr. Felton, did not participate in its inception. Now, in terms of the specifications, in terms of the demands that were made and met, we agreed not to send any observers into the reservation for a period of fifteen years. Of course, during those fifteen years there have been many conferences with Mr. and Mrs. Arbalaid and with certain of their associates, including Dr. Goldbaum."

"Then, if there were conferences," Felton said, "it seems to me that you know more about my sister than I do. You must understand that I have not seen my sister almost since the inception of the project."

"We understand that. Nevertheless, the relationship differs. Out of these conferences, Mr. Felton, there was no progress report that dealt with anything more than general progress and that in the most fuzzy and indefinite terms. We were given to understand that the results they had obtained in the reservation were quite rewarding and exciting, but little more, very little more indeed."

"That was to be expected. That's the way my sister works; in fact, it's the way most scientists work. They are engaged in something that is very special to them, very complicated, very difficult to explain. They do not like to give reports of the way stations they may arrive at. They like to complete their work and have results, proven results, before they report."

"We are aware of that, Mr. Felton. We honored our part of the agreement, and at the end of a fifteen-year period

we told your sister and her husband that they would have to
honor their part of the agreement and that we would have
to send in a team of observers. We were as liberal, as flex-
ible, as people in our position could be. We advised them
that they would have the right to choose the observers, that
they could even limit the path of the observers—limit what
the observers would see and the questions the observers
could ask—but that we would have to send in such a team."

"And did you?" Felton asked him.

"No, we did not. That's a tribute to the persuasive
powers of your sister and her husband. They pleaded for
an extension of time, maintaining that it was critical to the
success of the entire program, and they pleaded so per-
suasively that in the end they did win a three-year extension. Some months ago, the three-year period of grace was
over. Mrs. Arbalaid came to Washington and begged for a
further extension. I was at the meeting where she was heard,
and I can tell you, Mr. Felton, that never before in my life
had I heard a woman plead for something with the fervor,
the insistence, with which Mrs. Arbalaid pleaded for this
further extension."

Felton nodded. "Yes, I imagine my sister would plead
with some intensity. Did you agree?"

"No. As I said, we refused."

"You mean you turned her down completely—entirely?"

"Not as completely perhaps as we should have. She
agreed—when she saw that she could not move us—that our
team could come into the reservation in ten days. She
begged the ten-day interval to discuss the matter with her

husband and to choose the two people who would make up the observation team. The way she put it, we had to agree to it; and then she returned to California."

Eggerton paused and looked at Felton searchingly.

"Well," Felton said, "what happened then? Did my sister select competent observers?"

"You don't know?" Eggerton asked him.

"I know some things. I'm afraid I don't know whatever you're interested in at this moment. I certainly don't know what happened."

"That was three weeks ago, Mr. Felton. Your sister never chose observers; your sister never communicated with us again; in fact, we know nothing about your sister or her reactions or what she said to her husband because we have not heard from her since."

"That's rather curious."

"That is exceedingly curious, Mr. Felton, far more curious than you might imagine."

"Tell me, what did you do when ten days went by and you didn't hear from my sister?"

"We waited a few days more to see whether it was an oversight on her part, and then we tried to communicate with her."

"Well?"

"We couldn't. You know something, Felton? When I think about what I'm going to tell you now I feel like a damn fool. I also feel a little bit afraid. I don't know whether the fear or the fool predominates. Naturally, when we couldn't communicate with your sister, we went there."

"Then you did go there," Felton said.

"Oh, yes, we went there."

"And what did you find?"

"Nothing."

"I don't understand," Felton said.

"Didn't I make myself plain, Mr. Felton? We went there and we found nothing."

"Oh?"

"You don't appear too surprised, Mr. Felton."

"Nothing my sister did ever really surprised me. You mean the reservation was empty—no sign of anything, Mr. Eggerton?"

"No, I don't mean that at all, Mr. Felton. I wish to God I did mean that. I wish it were so pleasantly human and down to earth and reasonable. I wish we thought or had some evidence that your sister and her husband were two clever and unscrupulous swindlers who had taken the Government for a hundred and fourteen million dollars. That would have been a joy, Mr. Felton. That would have warmed the cockles of our hearts compared to what we do have and what we did find. You see, we don't know whether the reservation is empty or not, Mr. Felton, because the reservation is not there."

"What?"

"Precisely. Exactly what I said. The reservation is not there."

"Oh, come on now," Felton smiled. "My sister is a remarkable woman, but she doesn't make off with eight thousand acres of land. It isn't like her."

"I don't find your humor entertaining at this moment, Mr. Felton."

"No. No, of course not. I'm sorry. I realize that this is hardly the moment for humor. Only a thing is put to me and the thing makes no sense at all—how could an eight-thousand-acre stretch of land not be where it was? Doesn't that leave a damn big hole?"

"It's still a joke, isn't it, Mr. Felton?"

"Well, how do you expect me to react?" Felton asked.

"Oh, you're quite justified, Mr. Felton. If the news-papers got hold of it, they could do even better."

"Supposing you explain it to me," Felton said. "We're both guessing, aren't we? Maybe we're both putting each other on, maybe we're not. Let's be sensible about it and talk in terms that we both understand."

"All right," the Secretary said, "suppose you let me try, not to explain—that's beyond me—but to describe. The stretch of land where the reservation is located is in the Fulton National Forest: rolling country, some hills, a good stand of sequoia—a kidney-shaped area all in all, and very exclusive in terms of the natural formation. It's a sort of valley, a natural valley, that contains within itself areas of high land, areas of low land, and flat areas as well. Water, too. It was wire-fenced. Around it was a three-hundred-yard wide neutral zone, and Army guards were stationed at every possible approach. I went out there last week with our inspection team: General Meyers; two Army physicians; Gorman, the psychiatrist; Senator Totenwell of the Armed Services Committee; and Lydia Gentry, the educator who is our present Secretary of Education. You will admit that we had a comprehensive and intelligent team that repre-sented a fine cross-section of American society. At least,

Mr. Felton, that is my opinion. I still have some veneration for the American society."

"I share your admiration, Mr. Secretary, if not your veneration. I don't think that this should be a contest between you and me, *re* our attitudes toward the United States of America."

"No such contest intended, Mr. Felton. Let me continue. We crossed the country by plane and then we drove the final sixty miles to the reservation. We drove this distance in two Government cars. A dirt road leads into the reservation. The main guard, of course, is on that dirt road, and that road is the only road into the reservation, the only road that a vehicle could possibly take to go into the reservation. The armed guard on this road halted us, of course. They were merely doing their duty. The reservation was directly before us. The sergeant in charge of the guard approached the first car according to orders; and, as he walked toward our car, the reservation disappeared."

"Come on now," Felton said.

"I am trying to be reasonable and polite, Mr. Felton. I think the very least you could do is attempt to adopt the same attitude towards me. I said, 'The reservation disappeared.' "

"Just like that?" Felton whispered. "No noise—no explosion—no earthquake?"

"No noise, no explosion, no earthquake, Mr. Felton. One moment a forest of sequoia in front of us—then a gray area of nothing."

"Nothing. Nothing is not a fact, Mr. Secretary.

Nothing is not even a description; it's simply a word and a highly abstract word."

"We have no other word for this situation."

"Well, you say 'nothing.' What do you mean? Did you try to go in? If there was nothing in front of you, did you try to go through this nothing?"

"Yes, we tried. You can be very certain that we tried, Mr. Felton, and since then the best scientists in America have tried. I do not like to speak about myself as a brave man, but certainly I am not a coward. Yet believe me, it took a while for me to get up enough courage to walk up to that gray edge of nothing and touch it."

"Then you touched it?"

"I touched it."

"If it was nothing, it seems to me you could hardly touch it. If you could touch it, it was something, certainly not nothing."

"If you wish, it was something. It blistered these three fingers."

He held out his hand for Felton to see. The first three fingers of his right hand were badly blistered.

"That looks like a burn," Felton said.

"It is a burn. No heat and no cold, nevertheless it burned my hand. That kind of thing sets you back, Felton."

"I can appreciate that," Felton said.

"I became afraid then, Mr. Felton. I think we all became afraid. We continue to be afraid. Do you understand, Mr. Felton? The world today represents a most delicate and terrible balance of power. When news comes to us that the Chinese have developed an atomic weapon, we become afraid. Out of necessity, our diplomatic attitude must reflect such fear and our attitude toward the Chinese must change. When the French began their atomic stockpile, our attitude toward the French changed. We are a pragmatic and a realistic administration, Mr. Felton, and we do not lie about fear or abjure power; we recognize fear and power, and we are very much afraid of that damn thing out there in California."

"I need not ask you if you tried this or that."

"We tried everything, Mr. Felton. You know, I'm a little ashamed to say this, and it is certainly damned well not for publication—I trust you will honor my request in that direction, Mr. Felton—?"

"I am not here as a reporter for the press," Felton said.

"Of course, yet this is very delicate, very delicate indeed. You asked whether we tried this or that. We tried things. We even tried a very small atomic bomb. Yes, Mr. Felton, we tried the sensible things and we tried the foolish things. We went into panic and we went out of panic and we tried everything we have and it all failed."

"And yet you have kept it a secret?"

"So far, Mr. Felton, we have kept it a secret," the Secretary agreed. "You cannot imagine what wire-pulling that took. We threw our weight here and there, and we threw our weight heavily, and we kept the secret—so far, Mr. Felton."

"Well, what about airplanes? You couldn't bar access to it from the air, could you? You couldn't cut off so wide a lane of air visibility that it would not be seen?"

"No, we immediately observed it from the air; you

can be sure we thought of that quickly enough. But when you fly above it you see nothing. As I said, the reservation is in a valley, and all you see is what appears to be mist lying in the valley. Perhaps it is mist—"

Felton leaned back and thought about it.

"Take your time," the Secretary said to him. "We are not rushing you, Mr. Felton, and believe me we are not pressuring you. We want your coöperation and, if you know what this is, we want you to tell us what it is."

Finally Felton asked him, "What do your people think it is?"

Eggerton smiled coldly and shook his head. "They don't know. There you are. At first, some of them thought it was some kind of force field. I have since learned that *force field* is a generic term for any area of positive action not understood too well. But when they tried to work it out mathematically, the mathematics wouldn't work. When they put it on the computers, the mathematics still refused to work. I don't know the math, Mr. Felton. I'm not a physicist and I'm not a mathematician, so I'm merely reporting what I have been told. And, of course, it's cold, and they're very upset about the fact that it's cold. It seems to confuse them no end. Terribly cold. Don't think only I am mumbling, Mr. Felton. As I said, I am neither a scientist nor a mathematician, but I can assure you that the scientists and the mathematicians also mumble. As for me, Mr. Felton, I am sick to death of the mumbling. I am sick to death of the double-talk and the excuses. And that's why we decided that you should come to Washington and talk with us. We thought that you might know about this thing that bars us from the reservation, and you might be able to tell us what it is or tell us how to get rid of it."

"I haven't the vaguest idea what it is," Felton said, "but even if I had, what on earth makes you think that I would tell you how to get rid of it?"

"Surely you don't think it's a good thing."

"How can I say whether it's a good thing or a bad thing?" Felton asked him. "I haven't the faintest notion of what it is, and I'm not sure that I know, in today's scheme of things, what is good or what is bad."

"Then you can't help us at all?"

"I didn't say that either. I just might be able to help you."

For the first time, Eggerton emerged from his lethargy, his depression. Suddenly he was excited and patient and overly cordial. He tried to force another drink on Felton. When Felton refused, he suggested that champagne be brought. Felton smiled at him, and the Secretary admitted that he was being childish.

"But you don't know how you have relieved me, Mr. Felton."

"I don't see why the little I said should relieve you. I certainly didn't intend to relieve you, and I don't know whether I can help you or not. I said I might help you."

Felton took a letter out of his pocket.

"This came from my sister," he said.

"You told me you had no letter from her in almost a year," the Secretary replied suspiciously.

"Exactly. And I have had this letter for almost a year." There was a note of sadness in Felton's voice. "I haven't

(174

opened it, Mr. Secretary, because when she sent it to me she enclosed it in a sealed envelope with a short letter. The letter said that she was well and quite happy, and that I was not to open or read the enclosed letter until it was absolutely necessary to do so. My sister is like that. We think the same way. I think that it's necessary now, don't you?"

The Secretary nodded slowly but said nothing. His eyes were fixed on Felton. Felton scanned the letter, turned it over, and then reached toward the Secretary's desk where there was a letter opener. The Secretary made no move to help him. Felton took the opener, slit the letter and took out a sheaf of onionskin paper. He opened this sheaf of paper and he began to read aloud.

Chapter Seventeen

June 12, 1964

My dear Harry:

As I write this, it is twenty-two years since I have seen you or spoken to you. How very long for two people who have such love and regard for each other as we do! And now that you have found it necessary to open this letter and read it, we must face the fact that in all probability we will never see each other again unless we are most fortunate. And, Harry, I have watched so many miracles occur that I hesitate to dream of another. I know from your letters that you have a wife and three children, and I have seen their photographs. So far as I can tell, they are wonderful people. I think the hardest thing is to know that I will not see them or come to know them and watch them grow, and at least be some sort of sister to your wife.

Only this thought saddens me. Otherwise, Mark and

I are very happy—perhaps as happy as two human beings have any right to be. As you read this letter I think you will come to understand why.

Now, about the barrier—which must exist or you would not have opened the letter—tell them that there is no harm to it and that no hurt will be caused by it. The very worst that can happen is that if one leans against it too long, one's skin may be badly blistered. But the barrier cannot be broken into because it is a negative power rather than a positive one, an absence instead of a presence. I will have more to say about it later, but I don't think I will be able to explain it better. My physics is limited, and these are things for which we, as human beings, have no real concepts. To put it into visual terms or understandable terms for a layman is almost impossible—at least for me. I imagine that some of the children could put it into intelligible words, but I want this to be my report, not theirs.

Strange that I still call them children and think of them as children—when in all fact we are the children and they are the adults. But they still have the quality of children that we know best: the innocence and purity that vanishes so quickly with the coming of puberty in the outside world.

Now, dear Harry, I must tell you what came of our experiment—or some of it. Some of it, for how could I ever put down the story of the strangest two decades that man ever lived through? It is all incredible and, at the same time, it is all commonplace. We took a group of wonderful children and we gave them an abundance of love, security and truth—but I think it was the factor of love that mattered most, and because we were able to give them these three very obvious things—love, security and truth—we were able to return to them their heritage, and what a heritage it is, Harry!

During the first year we weeded out those couples who showed less than a total desire to love the children. I mention this because you must not think that any stage of this was easy or that any part of it ran smoothly. We went into the reservation with twenty-three couples; six of them— that is, twelve people—failed to meet our test, and they had to go, but they were still good people and they abided by the necessity for silence and security.

But our children are easy to love, and they were easy to love from the very beginning. You see, I call them our children, Harry, because as the years passed they became our children—in every way. The children who were born to the couples in residence here simply joined the group. No one had a father or a mother; we were a living, functioning group in which all the men were the fathers of all the children and all the women were the mothers of all the children.

Now this is very easy to state as a fact, Harry; it is easy to project as a concept; but its achievement was far from easy. Its achievement was something that tore us to pieces. We had to turn ourselves inside out, totally reëxamine ourselves, to achieve this. This among ourselves, Harry, among the adults who had to fight and work and examine each other inside and outside again and again and again—and tear out our guts and tear our hearts out—so that we could present ourselves to the children as something in the way of human beings. I mean a quality of sanity and truth and security embodied in a group of adult men and women. Far more spectacular achievements than this were accomplished, Harry—but perhaps nothing more wonderful than the fact that we, the adults, could remake ourselves. In doing so, we gave the children their chance.

And what did the chance amount to? How shall I tell you of an American Indian boy, five years old, composing a splendid symphony? Or of the two children, one Bantu, one Italian, one a boy, one a girl, who at the age of six built a machine to measure the speed of light? Will you believe that we, the adults, sat quietly and respectfully and listened to these six-year-olds explain to us a new theory of light? We listened, and perhaps some of us understood, but most of us did not. I certainly did not. I might translate it and repeat it in these terms—that since the speed of light is a constant anywhere, regardless of the motion of material bodies, the distance between the stars cannot be mentioned or determined in terms of the speed of light, since distance so arrived at is not, and has no equivalence to, distance on our plane of being. Does what I have said make any sense to you? It makes just a little to me. If I put it poorly, awkwardly, blame my own ignorance.

I mention just this one small thing. In a hundred—no, in a thousand—of these matters, I have had the sensations of an uneducated immigrant whose beloved child is exposed to all the wonders of school and knowledge. Like this immigrant, I understand a little of what the children achieve, but very little indeed. If I were to repeat instance after instance, wonder after wonder—at the ages of six and seven and eight and nine—would you think of the poor, tortured, nervous creatures whose parents boast that they have an IQ of 160 or of 170 and, in the same breath, bemoan the fate that did not give them normal children? Do you understand me, Harry? These children of ours, in your world, would have been condemned to disaster—not to simple disaster but to the specific, terrible disaster that befalls the super-knowing, the super-sensitive, the super-intelligent who are ground down, degraded and destroyed just as that Assamese child raised by the wolves was destroyed. Well, our children were and are normal children. Perhaps they are the first truly normal children that this world has seen in a long time—in many thousands of years. If just once you could hear them laugh or sing, you would know how absolutely true my statement is. If only you could see how tall and strong they are, how fine of body and movement. They have a quality that I have never seen in children before.

I suppose, dear Harry, that much about them would shock you just as it would shock most of the population of the outside world. Most of the time, they wear no clothes. Sex has always been a joy and a good thing to them, and they face it and enjoy it as naturally as we eat and drink—more naturally, for we have no gluttons in sex or food, no ulcers of the belly or the soul.

Our children kiss and caress each other and do many other things that the world has specified as shocking, nasty, forbidden, dirty, obscene. But whatever they do, they do it with grace and they do it with joy, and they have no guilt nor any knowledge whatsoever of guilt. *Guilt* as word or fact is meaningless to them.

Is all this possible? Or is it a dream and an illusion? I tell you that it has been my life for almost twenty years now. I live with these children, with boys and girls who are without evil or sickness, who are like pagans or gods, however you would look at it.

But the story of the children and of their day-to-day life is one that will some day be told properly in its own time and place. Certainly I have neither the time nor the ability to tell it here, Harry. You will have to content yourself with the bits and snatches that I can put down in this letter to you. All the indications that I have put down here add up only to great gifts and great abilities. But, after all, this was inherent in the children we selected. Mark and I never had any doubts about such results; we knew that if we created a controlled environment that was predicated on our hypothesis, the children would learn more than children do on the outside.

Naturally, this part of it came about. How could it have been otherwise—unless, of course, Mark and I had flubbed the whole thing and acted like fools and sentimentalists. But I don't think that there was much danger of that. Without being egotistical I can say that we, and of course Professor Goldbaum (who was with us through all the most difficult years), and our associates—we knew what we were doing. We knew precisely what we were doing and we knew pretty well how to do it.

In the seventh year of their lives, the children were dealing easily and naturally with scientific problems normally taught on the college level or on the postgraduate level in the outside world. But, as I said, this was to be expected, this was normal and we would have been very disappointed indeed if this development had not taken place. It was the unexpected that we hoped for, prayed for, dreamed of and watched for. A flowering, a development of the mind of man that was unpredictable and unknowable, which we could comprehend only negatively by theorizing that a block to such development is locked in every single human being on the outside.

And it came. Originally, it began with a Chinese child in the fifth year of our work. The second incident occurred in an American child, and the third in a Burmese child. Most strangely, it was not thought of as anything very unusual by the children themselves. We did not realize what was happening until the seventh year, that is, two years after the process had begun; and by that time it had happened already in five of the children. The very fact that it took place so gently, so naturally, so obviously, was a healthy symptom.

Let me tell you how we discovered what was happening. Mark and I were taking a walk that day—I remember it so well, a lovely, cool and clear northern California day—when we came upon a group of children in a meadow. There were about a dozen children gathered together in the meadow. Five of the children sat in a little circle, with a sixth child in the center of their circle. The six heads were almost touching. They were full of little giggles, ripples of mirth and satisfaction. The rest of the children sat in a group about ten feet away—watching intently, seriously, respectfully.

As we came closer the children were neither alarmed

nor disturbed. The children in the second group put their
fingers to their lips, indicating that we should be quiet. So
we came rather close, and then we stood and watched without speaking.

After we were there about ten minutes, the little girl
in the center of the circle of five children leaped to her feet,
crying out ecstatically:

"I heard you! I heard you! I heard you!"

There was a kind of achievement and delight reflected
in the sound of her voice that we had not experienced
before, not even from our children. Then all of the children
there rushed together to kiss and embrace the girl who had
been in the middle of the group of five. They did a sort of
dance of play and delight around her. All this we watched
with no indication of surprise or even very great curiosity
on our part. For even though this was the first time anything like this—anything beyond our expectation or comprehension—had ever happened, we had worked out what
our own reaction should be to such discoveries and achievements on the part of the children. We had made up our
minds that whatever they accomplished, our position would
be that it was perfectly natural and completely expected.

When the children rushed to us for our congratula-
tions, we nodded and smiled and agreed that it was all very
wonderful.

"Whose turn is it now?" Mark asked.

They called all the men "Father," the women
"Mother." A Senegalese boy turned to me and said excit-
edly, "Now, it's my turn, Mother. I can do—well, I can

almost do it already. Now there are six to help me, and it will be much easier."

"Aren't you proud of us?" another child cried.

"So proud," I said. "We couldn't be more proud."

"Are you going to do it now?" Mark asked him.

"Not now, we're tired now. You know, when you go at it with a new one, it's terribly tiring. After that, it's not tiring. But the first time it is."

"Then when will you do it?" I asked.

"Maybe tomorrow."

"Can we be here? I mean would you want us here when you do it or does it make it harder?"

"No harder," one of them said.

"Of course you can be here," another answered. "We would like you to be here."

"Both of us?" Mark asked.

"Of course, both of you and any other mother or father who wants to come."

We pressed it no further, but that evening at our regular staff meeting Mark described what had happened and repeated the conversation.

"I noticed the same thing a few weeks ago," Mary Hengel, our semantics teacher, said. "I watched them, but either they didn't see me or they didn't mind my watching them."

"Did you go up close to them?" I asked her.

"No, I was a little uncertain about that. I must have stayed about forty or fifty yards away."

"How many were there then?" Professor Goldbaum

asked Mary Hengel. He was very intent on his question, smiling slightly.

"Three. No, there was a fourth child in the center—the three had their heads together. I simply thought it was one of their games—they have so many—and I walked away after a little while."

"They make no secret about it," someone else observed.

"Yes," I said, "we had the same feeling. They just took it for granted that we knew what they were doing, and they were quite proud of what they were doing."

"The interesting thing is," Mark said, "that while they were doing it, no one spoke. I can vouch for that."

"Yet they were listening," I put in. "There is no question about that; they were listening and they were listening for something, and finally, I imagine, they heard what they were listening for. They giggled and they laughed as if some great joke were taking place—you know the way children laugh about a game that delights them."

"Of course," said Abel Simms, who was in charge of our construction program, "of course they have no knowledge of right and wrong in our terms, and nothing they do ever seems wrong to them, just as nothing they do ever seems right to them; so there is no way to gauge their attitude in that sense toward whatever they were doing."

We discussed it a bit further, and it was Dr. Goldbaum who finally put his finger on it. He said, very gravely:

"Do you know, Jean—you always thought and hoped and dreamed too that we might open that great area of the human mind that is closed and blocked in all human beings.

I think they found out how to open it. I think they are teaching each other and learning from each other what is to them a very simple and obvious thing—how to listen to thoughts."

There was a rather long silence after that, and then Atwater, one of our psychologists, said uneasily, "I am not sure I believe it. You know, I have investigated every test and every report on telepathy ever published in this country, and as much as I could gather and translate of what was published in other parts of the world—the Duke experiments and all the rest of it. None of it, absolutely none of it, was dependable, and absolutely none of it gave any provable or reliable or even believable evidence or indication that such a thing as mental telepathy exists. You know, we have measured brain waves. We know how tiny and feeble they are —it just seems to me utterly fantastic that brain waves can be a means of communication."

"Hold on there," said Tupper, an experimental physicist. "The seemingly obvious linkage of brain waves with telepathy is rather meaningless, you know. If telepathy exists, it is not a result of what we call brain waves of the tiny electric pattern that we are able to measure. It's quite a different type of action, in a different manner on a wholly different level of physical reality. Just what that level is, I have no idea. But one of the things we are learning more and more certainly in physics is that there are different levels of reality, different levels of action and interaction of force and counterforce, so we cannot dispose of telepathy by citing brain waves."

"But how about the statistical factor?" Rhoda Lannon,

a mathematician, argued. "If this faculty existed, even as a potential in mankind, is it conceivable that there would be no recorded instance of it? Statistically it must have emerged not once but literally thousands of times."

"Maybe it has been recorded," said Fleming, one of our historians. "Can you take all the whippings and burnings and hangings of history, all the witches, the demigods, the magicians, the alchemists, and determine which of these were telepaths and which were not? Also, there is another way of looking at it. Suppose one telepath alone is totally impotent. Suppose we need two telepaths to make it work, and suppose there is a limited distance over which two telepaths can operate. Then the statistical factor becomes meaningless and the accident becomes virtually impossible."

"I think that all in all I agree at least to some extent with Dr. Goldbaum," Mark said. "The children are becoming telepaths. It seems to me there is no question about that; it is the only sensible explanation for what Jean and I witnessed. If you argue, and with reason, that our children do not react to right and wrong and have no real understanding of right and wrong, then we must also add that they are equally incapable of lying. They have no understanding of the lie, of the meaning of the lie or of the necessity of the lie. So, if they told me that they heard what is not spoken, I have to believe them. I am not moved by an historical argument or by a statistical argument, because our concentration here is the environment and the absolute singularity of our environment. I speak of an historical singularity. There is no record in all of human history of a similar group of unusual children being raised in such an environment. Also, this may be—and probably is—a faculty of man which must be released in childhood, or remain permanently blocked. I believe Dr. Haenigson here will bear me out when I say that mental blocks imposed during childhood are not uncommon."

"More than that," Dr. Haenigson, our chief psychiatrist, stated. "No child in our history escapes the need to erect mental blocks in his mind. Without the ability to erect such blocks, it is safe to say that very few children in our society would survive. Indeed, we must accept the fact—and this is not theoretical or hypothetical, this is a fact, a provable fact which we have learned as psychiatrists—that whole areas of the mind of every human being are blocked in early childhood. This is one of the tragic absolutes of human society, and the removal—not the total removal, for that is impossible, but the partial removal—of such blocks becomes the largest part of the work of practicing psychiatrists."

Dr. Goldbaum was watching me strangely. I was about to say something, but I stopped and I waited, and finally Dr. Goldbaum said:

"I wonder whether we have begun to realize what we may have done without even knowing what we were doing. That is the wonderful, the almost unbearable implication of what may have happened here. What is a human being? He is the sum of his memories and his experience—these are locked in his brain, and every moment of experience simply builds up the structure of these memories. We do not know as yet what is the extent or power of the gift these children of ours appear to be developing, but suppose they reach a point where they can easily and naturally share the totality of memory? It is not simply that among themselves there can be no lies, no deceit, no rationalization, no secrets, no guilts—it is far more than that."

Then he looked from face to face, around the whole circle of our staff. At that point we were beginning to understand him and comprehend the condition he was posing. I remember my own reactions at that moment: a sense of wonder and discovery and joy, and heartbreak too, a feeling so poignant that it brought tears to my eyes. But above and beyond all that, I felt a sense of excitement, of enormous and exhilarating excitement.

"You know, I see," Dr. Goldbaum said. "I think that all of you know to one degree or another. Perhaps it would be best for me to speak about it, to put it into words, and to open it up to our thinking. I am much older than any of you—and I have been through and lived through the worst years of horror and bestiality that mankind ever knew. When I saw what I saw, when I witnessed the rise of Hitlerism, the concentration camps, the abattoirs, the ovens, the senseless, meaningless madness that culminated in the use of human skin to make lampshades, of human flesh and fat to make soap, when I saw and watched all this, I asked myself a thousand times: What is the meaning of mankind? Or has it any meaning at all? Is man not, perhaps, simply a haphazard accident, an unusual complexity of molecular structure, a complexity without meaning, without purpose and without hope? I know that you all have asked yourselves the same thing perhaps a hundred, a thousand times. What sensitive or thoughtful human being does not ask this question of himself? Who are we? What are we? What is our destiny? What is our purpose? Where is sanity or reason in these bits of struggling, clawing, sick, murderous flesh? We kill, we torture, we hurt, we destroy as no other species does. We ennoble murder and falsehood and hypocrisy and superstition. We destroy our own bodies with drugs and poisonous food. We deceive ourselves as well as others. And we hate and hate and hate until every action we take is a result of our hatred.

"Now something has happened. Something new, something different, something very wonderful. If these children can go into each other's minds completely, then they will have a single memory, which is the memory of all of them. All their experience will be common to all of them, all their knowledge will be common to all of them, all the dreams they dream will be common to all of them—and do you know what that means? It means that they will be immortal. For as one of them dies, another child is linked to the whole, and another, and another. For them there will be no death. Death will lose all of its meaning, all of its dark horror. Mankind will begin, here in this place, in this strange little experiment of ours, to fulfill at least one part of its intended destiny—to become a single, wonderful thing, a whole—almost in the old words of your poet, John Donne, who sensed what each of us has sensed at one time or another: that no man is an island unto himself. Our tragedy has been that we are singular. We never lived, we were always fragmented bits of flesh at the edge of reality, at the edge of life. Tell me, has any thoughtful man or woman ever lived life without having a sense of that singleness of mankind and longing for it and dreaming of it? I don't think so. I think we have all had it, and therefore we have, all of us, been living in darkness, in the night, each of us struggling with his own poor little brain and then dying, perishing, with all the memories and work of a lifetime destroyed forever. It is no wonder that we achieve so little. The wonder is that we have achieved so much. Yet all that we know, all that we have done, will be nothing, primitive, idiotic, nothing compared to what these children will know and do and create. It just staggers my imagination."

So the old man spelled it out, Harry. I can't put it all down here, but do you know, he saw it—at that moment, which was almost the beginning of it, he saw it in all of its far-flung implications. I suppose that was his reward, that he was able to fling his imagination forward into the future, the vast unrealized future, and see the blinding, incredible promise that it holds for us.

Well, that was the beginning, Harry; within the next twelve months, each one of our children was linked to all of the others telepathically. And in the years that followed, every child born in our reservation was shown the way into that linkage by the children. Only we, the adults, were forever barred from joining it. We were of the old and they were of the new. Their way was closed to us forever —although they could go into our minds, and did when they had to. But never could we feel them there or see them there or go into their minds or communicate with them as they did with each other.

I don't know how to tell you of the years that followed, Harry. In our little guarded reservation, man became what he was always destined to be, but I can explain it only imperfectly. I can hardly comprehend, much less explain, what it means to inhabit forty bodies simultaneously, or what it means to each of the children to have the other personalities within him or her, a part of each of them. Can I even speculate on what it means to live as man and woman, always together, not only in the flesh, but man and woman within the same mind?

Could the children explain it to us? Did they explain it to us? Hardly. For this is a transformation that must take place, from all we can learn, before puberty; and as it happens, the children accept it as normal and natural—indeed as the most natural thing in the world. We were the unnatural ones—and the one thing they never truly comprehended is how we could bear to live in our aloneness, how we could bear to live on the edge of death and extinction and with the knowledge of death and extinction always pressing against us. Again, could we explain to a man born blind what color is, gradations of color, form, light, or the meaning of light and form combined? Hardly, any more than they are able to explain their togetherness to us who live so singularly and so alone.

As for the children's knowledge of us, we are very happy, indeed grateful that it did not come at once. In the beginning, the children could merge their thoughts only when their heads were almost touching. This is what saved them from us, because if, in the very beginning, they had been able to touch our thoughts, they might not have been able to defend themselves. Bit by bit, their command of distance grew, but very slowly; and not until our fifteenth year in the reservation did the children begin to develop the power to reach out and probe with their thoughts anywhere on earth. We thank God for this. By then the children were ready for what they found. Earlier, it might have destroyed them.

I might mention here that the children explained to us in due time that their telepathic powers had nothing to do with brain waves. Telepathy, according to the children, is a function of time, but exactly what that means, I don't know, Harry, and therefore I cannot explain it to you.

I must mention that two of our children met accidental death—one in the ninth year and the second in the eleventh year. But the effects of these two deaths upon the other children cannot be compared to the effects of death in our world. There was a little regret, but no grief, no sense of great loss, no tears or weeping. Death is totally different among them than among us; among them, a loss of flesh and only flesh; the personality itself is immortal and lives consciously in the others.

When we spoke to them about a marked grave, or a tombstone, or some other mark that would enable us to keep alive the memory of the two dead children, they smiled sympathetically and said that we could make such a tomb or tombstone if it would give us any comfort. Their concern was only for us, not in any way for the two bodies that were gone.

Yet later, when Dr. Goldbaum died, their grief was deep and terrible, something so deep, so heartbreaking, that it touched us more than anything in our whole experience here—and this, of course, was because Dr. Goldbaum's death was the old kind of death.

The strangest thing, Harry, is that in spite of all these indications and means of togetherness that I have been telling you about, outwardly our children remain individuals. Each of the children retains his or her own characteristics, mannerisms and personality. The boys and the girls make love in a normal, heterosexual manner—though all of them share the experience. Can you comprehend that? I cannot; but then neither can I comprehend any other area of their emotional experience except to realize that for them everything is different. Only the unspoiled devotion of mother for helpless child can approximate the love that binds them together. Yet here, too, in their love everything is different, deeper than anything that we can relate to our own experience. Before their transformation into telepaths took place, the children displayed enough petulance and anger and annoyance; but after it took place, we never again heard a voice raised in anger or annoyance. As they themselves put it, when there was trouble among them, they washed it out. When there was sickness among them, they healed it.

After the ninth year, there was no more sickness. By then they had learned to control their bodies. If sickness approached their bodies—and by that I mean infection, germs, virus, whatsoever you might call it—they could control and concentrate the reaction of their bodies to infection; and with such conscious control and such conscious ability to change the chemical balance of their bodies, to change their heartbeat if necessary, to influence their blood flow, to increase the circulation in one part of the body, to decrease it in another, to increase or decrease the functioning of various organs in the body—with that kind of control, they were absolutely immune to sickness. However, they could go further than that. While they could give us no part of the wholeness which they enjoyed as a normal thing of their lives, they could cure our illnesses. Three or four of them would merge their minds and go into our bodies and cure our bodies. They would go into our minds; they would control the organs of our bodies and the balance of our bodies and cure them; and yet we, the recipients of this cure, were never aware of their presence.

In trying to describe all of this to you, Harry, to make it real and to make incidents come alive, I use certain words and phrases only because I have no other words and phrases, I have no language that fits the life of these children. I use the words I know, but at the same time I realize, and you must realize, that my words do not describe adequately—they do not serve the use I am trying to put them to. Even after all these years of living intimately with the children, day and night, I can comprehend only vaguely the manner of their existence. I know what they are outwardly because I see it, I watch it. They are free and healthy and happy as no men and women ever were before. But what their inner life is remains a closed thing to me.

Again and again we discussed this with various members of our group, that is, among ourselves and also among the children. The children had no reticence about it; they were willing, eager, delighted to discuss it with us, but the discussions were hardly ever fruitful. For example, take the conversation I had with one of the children, whose name is Arlene. She is a tall, lovely child whom we found in an orphanage in Idaho. She came to us as the other children did, in infancy. At the time of our conversation, Arlene was fourteen. So much, you see, had happened in the reservation during the intervening years. We were discussing personality, and I told Arlene that I could not understand how she could live and work as an individual when she was also a part of so many others, and these so many others were a part of her.

She, however, could not see that and she rejected the whole concept.

"But how can you be yourself?" I pressed her.

"I remain myself," she answered simply. "I could not stop being myself."

"But aren't the others also yourself?"

"Yes, of course, what else could they be? And I am also them."

This was put to me as something self-evident. You see, it is no easier for them to understand our concepts than it is for us to understand their concepts. I said to her then:

"But who controls your body?"

"I do, of course."

"But just for the sake of a hypothetical situation, Arlene, suppose we take this possibility—that some of the other children should want to control your body instead of leaving the control to you."

"Why?" she asked me.

"If you did something they didn't approve of," I said lamely, digging the hole I had gotten into still deeper.

"Something they disapproved of?" she asked. "Well, how could I? Can you do something that you yourself disapprove of?"

"I am afraid I can, Arlene, and I do."

"Now that I don't understand at all, Jean. Why do you do it?"

"Well, don't you see, I can't always control what I do."

This was a new notion to her. Even able to read our minds, this was a new notion to her.

"You can't control what you do?" she asked.

"Not always."

"Poor Jean," she said, "oh, poor Jean. How terrible. What an awful way to have to live."

"But it's not so terrible, Arlene," I argued, "not at all. For us it's perfectly normal."

"But how? How could such things be normal?"

So these discussions always seemed to develop and so they always ended. The communication between us, with all the love that the children had for us and all the love that we had for the children, was so limited. We, the adults, had only words for communication; and words are very limited. But by their tenth year, the children had developed methods of communication as far beyond words as words are beyond the dumb motions of animals. If one of them watched something, there was no necessity to describe what he or she watched to the others. The others could see it through the eyes of the child who was watching. This went on not only in waking but in sleeping as well. They actually dreamed together, participated in the same dreams.

Has it ever occurred to you, Harry, that when something hurts you, you don't have to engage in conversation with yourself to tell yourself that it hurts you? When you have a certain feeling, you don't have to explain the feeling to yourself; you have the feeling. And this was the process of communication that was perfectly natural to the children. They felt as a unit, as a body, and yet they remained individuals.

I could go on for hours attempting to describe something utterly beyond my understanding, but that would not help, would it, Harry? You will have your own problems, and I must try to make you understand what happened, what had to happen, and now what must happen in the future.

You see, Harry, by the tenth year, the children had learned all we knew, all we had among us as material for teaching; our entire pooled experience was now used up. In effect, we were teaching a single mind, a mind composed of the unblocked, unfettered talent and brains of forty superb children. Consider that. A mind forty times as large, as agile, as comprehensive as any mind that man had ever known before—a mind so rational, so pure, that to this mind we could only be objects of loving pity. We have among us, as a pair of our group parents, Alex Cromwell and his wife. You will recognize Alex Cromwell's name; he is one of our greatest physicists, and it was he who was largely responsible for the first atom bomb. After that, he came to us as one would go to a monastery. He performed an act of personal expiation in the only manner which could give him any hope, any satisfaction, any surcease from the enormous and terrible guilt that he bore. He and his wife taught our children physics, but by the eighth year, mind you, by the eighth year of their lives, the children were teaching Cromwell. A year later, Cromwell could no longer he taught. He was now incapable of following either their mathematics or their reasoning, and their symbolism, of course, was totally outside of the structure of Cromwell's thoughts. Imagine a mind like Cromwell's, led with concern, with tenderness, with gentleness, with the greatest love and consideration that the children could give him —for he is a charming and lovable person—imagine that such a mind could not advance within the area of knowledge that these nine-year-old children possessed.

It is rather terrifying, isn't it? And when you will show this letter (and of course we want you to show this letter) to the people who command the destiny of the United States, this thing I have just written will also be terrifying to them. I think that one of the saddest aspects of our society is the fear of the child that it engenders in the adult. That is a continuing fact of our society. Each generation, as it matures, fears the coming generation, looks at the coming generation as being conscienceless and depraved. No skill of adults, no talent of adults will engender as much fear as this skill, this talent, this brilliance of our children. Remember that, Harry, and expect it.

Let me give you an example of some of the capabilities, some of the powers our children have developed. In the far outfield of our baseball diamond, there was a boulder of perhaps ten tons. Incidentally, I must remark that our children's athletic skill, their physical prowess, is in its own way almost as extraordinary as their mental powers. They have broken every track and field record, often cutting world records by one third and even by one half. I have watched them effortlessly run down our horses. Their movements and their reactions are so quick as to make us appear sluggards by comparison. If they so desire, they can move their arms and legs faster than our eyes can follow; and, of course, one of the games they love is baseball, and they play in a manner you have never seen on the outside. Now to go back to this situation of the boulder: For some years we, the adults, had spoken of either blasting the boulder apart or of rolling it out of the way with one of our very heavy bulldozers, but it was something we had simply never gotten to. Then, one day, we discovered that the boulder was gone, and in its place was a pile of thick red dust—a pile that the wind was fast leveling.

We brooded over the matter ourselves for a while, made our usual attempt at interpretation, made our guesses, and at last, frustrated, went to the children and asked them what had happened. They told us that they had reduced the boulder to dust—as if it were no more than kicking a small stone out of one's path and just as if everyone could at will reduce a gigantic boulder to dust. Why not?

Cromwell cornered them on this one and he asked one of the children, Billy:

"But how? After all, Billy, you say you reduced the boulder to dust, but how? That's the point. How?"

"Well, the ordinary way," Billy said.

"You mean there's an ordinary way to reduce a boulder to dust?"

"Well, isn't there?" another child asked.

Billy was more patient. He sensed our difficulty and asked gently whether perhaps Cromwell did not know the ordinary way, but had to do it in some more complex way.

"I suppose I could reduce the boulder to dust," Cromwell said. "I would have to use a great deal of heavy explosive. It would take some time; it would make a lot of noise; and it would be rather expensive."

"But the end would be the same, wouldn't it?" Billy asked.

"I suppose so," Cromwell said, "if you mean dust."

"No, I mean the manner," Billy said, "the technique."

"What technique?" Cromwell asked desperately.

"Well, our technique. I mean to make anything dust you have to unbond it. We do it by loosening the molecular structure—not very quickly, you know, it could be dangerous if you did it too quickly—but we just loosen it slowly, steadily, and we let the thing kick itself to pieces, so to speak. That doesn't mean that it actually kicks itself to pieces. It doesn't explode or anything of that sort; it just powders away. You know, it holds its shape for a while, and then you touch it and it becomes powder—it collapses."

"But how do you do it?" Cromwell insisted.

"Well, the best way of course—directly. I mean with your mind. You understand it, and then you reject it as an understood phenomenon and you let it shake itself loose."

But the more he spoke, the further Billy traveled from Cromwell's area of comprehension; the more he used words, the less the words were able to convey. And finally, with patient and sympathetic smiles, the children dismissed the whole thing and their attempt to enlighten us as well. This was what usually happened, and this was the manner in which it usually happened.

Of course it was not always that way. They used the tools of our civilization, not because they admired these tools or because they needed mechanical things, but simply because they felt that our anxieties were eased by a certain amount of old-fashioned procedure. In other words, they wanted to preserve some of our world for our own sentimental needs. For example, they built an atomic-fusion power plant, out of which we derived and continued to derive our power. Then they built what they called free-fields into all our trucks and cars so that the trucks and cars could rise and travel through the air with the same facility as on the ground. The children could have built sensible, meaningful platforms that would have done the same thing and would have done it in a functional manner. The cars were much less functional; automobiles and trucks are not built to travel through the air. But the children had the kind of concern for the outer aspect of our world that led them to refrain from disarranging it too much.

At this point the use of thought, the degree to which they are able to use their own thoughts to influence atomic structure, is the most remarkable gift that they have beyond the power of telepathy itself. With the power of their thoughts they can go into atoms, they can control atoms, they can rearrange electrons; they can go into the enormous, almost infinite random patterns of electrons and atoms, and move things so that the random becomes directed and changes take place. In this way they are able to build one element out of another, and the curious thing of it is that all this is so elementary to them that they will do it at times as if they were doing tricks to amuse and amaze us, to save us from boredom, as an adult might do tricks for a child and so entertain the child.

So, dear Harry, I have been able to tell you something of what went on here over the years, a little bit of what the children are, a little bit about what they can do —not as much, perhaps, as I would want to tell you. I think I would like to create an hour-by-hour diary for you so that there might be a record on your side of what every day, every week of the last nineteen years has held; for, believe me, every day in every week of almost twenty years was exciting and rewarding.

Now I must tell you what you must know; and you shall tell these things to whoever you wish to tell them to. Use only your own judgment. Nothing in this document, Harry, is a secret. Nothing is for your ears alone. Nothing is to be held back. All of it can be given to the world. As for how much of it should be given to all the world, that must be a decision of the people who control the means of information. But let the decision be theirs, Harry. Do not interfere with it. Do not try to influence it; and above all, do not suppress anything that I am writing here.

In the fifteenth year of the experiment, our entire staff met with the children on a very important occasion. There were fifty-two children then, for all of the children born to us were taken into their body of singleness and flourished in their company. I must add that this was possible despite the initially lower IQ's of most of the children born to our mothers and fathers. Once the group has formed itself telepathically and has merged its powers, there is no necessity for high IQ's among the children who are brought into it. In fact, we are speculating on whether the experiment might not have proceeded almost the same way if we had chosen our first forty children at random. This we will never know.

Now, as to this meeting: It was a very formal and a very serious meeting, perhaps the most serious meeting of our experiment. Thirty days were left before the team of observers was scheduled to enter the reservation, according to the terms of our initial agreement with the Army. We had discussed that situation at great length among ourselves, the adults, and with the children, and of course it had been discussed among the children without us. But now it was discussed formally.

The children had chosen Michael to speak for them, but of course they were all speaking. Michael was simply the voice necessary to communicate with us. Michael, I might say, was born in Italy, a tall, delicate, lovely young man, and a most talented artist. Again I might mention that talent, specific talent, remained the property, the gift of the individual. This could not be communicated through the group to another child. Knowledge, yes, but a creative talent remained entirely the gift of the child who had it originally.

Michael took the floor and began by telling us how much the children loved and cherished us, the adults who were once their teachers.

I interrupted him to say that it was hardly necessary for the children ever to spell that out. We might not be able to communicate telepathically but never once was there anything in their actions to make us doubt their love for us.

"Of course," Michael said, "we understand that; yet,

at the same time, certain things must be said. They must be said in your language, and unless they are said they do not really exist as they must exist in relation to you. Believe us, we comprehend fully that all that we have, all that we are, you have given us. You are our fathers and mothers and teachers—and we love you beyond our power to say. We know that you consider us something superior to yourselves, something more than yourselves and beyond yourselves. This may be true, but it is also a fact of life that in each step forward, along with what is gained, something else is lost. There is a taking and a giving, a taking on and a putting aside. For years now, we have wondered and marveled at your patience and self-giving, for we have gone into your minds and we have known what pain and doubt and fear and confusion all of you live with. But there is something else that until now you have not known."

He paused and looked at each of us in turn. Then he looked at me searchingly, wonderingly, and I nodded as if to tell him to go ahead and tell us everything and hold nothing back.

"This then," Michael said. "We have also gone into the minds of the soldiers who guard the reservation. More and more, our power to probe grew and extended itself so that now, in this fifteenth year, there is no mind anywhere on earth that we cannot seek out and read. I need not tell you how many thousands of minds we have already sought out and read."

He paused, and I looked at Dr. Goldbaum who shook his head. Tears rolled down his cheeks and he whispered, "Oh my God, my God, what you must have seen. How could you do it and how could you bear it?"

"You never really knew how much we can bear," Michael said. "Always we had a child-parent relationship. It was a good relationship. Always you sought to protect us, to interpose your body, your presence, between ourselves and the world. But you didn't have to. It hurts me to say it, but you must know that long, long ago you became the children and we became the parents."

"We know it," I said. "Whether or not we spoke about it in so many words, we know it. We have known it for a long time."

"From our seventh year," Michael continued, "we knew all the details of this experiment. We knew why we were here and we knew what you were attempting—and from then until now, we have pondered over what our future must be. We have also tried to help you, whom we love so much, and perhaps we have been of some help in easing your discontents, in keeping you as physically healthy as possible, in helping you through your troubled, terrible nights and that maze of fear and nightmare and horror that you and all other human beings call sleep. We did what we could, but all our efforts to join you with us, to open your minds to each other and our minds to you, all these efforts have failed. Finally we learned that unless the necessary area of the mind is opened before puberty, the brain tissues change, the brain cells lose the potential of development and the mind is closed forever. Of all the things we face, this saddens us most—for you have given us the most precious heritage of mankind and, in return, we are able to give you nothing."

"That isn't so," I said. "You have given us more than we gave you, so much more."

"Perhaps," Michael nodded. "Or perhaps it helps for you to think that and to say that. You are very good and kind people. You have a kind of tenderness, a kind of gentle love that we can never have, for it grows out of your fear, your guilt, and the horror you live with. We have never been able, nor did we want, to know such fear, such guilt and such horror. It is foreign to us. So while we save ourselves the knowledge of these things, we are also deprived of the kind of love, the kind of self-sacrifice that is almost a matter-of-fact part of your nature. That we must say. But now, our fathers and our mothers, now the fifteen years are over; now this team of observers will be here in thirty days."

I shook my head and said quietly but firmly, "No. They must be stopped. They must not come here; they cannot come here."

"And all of you?" Michael asked, looking from one to another of us. "Do you all feel the same way? Do you all know what will come after that? Can you imagine what will come after that? Do you know what will happen in Washington? This is what you must think about now."

Some of us were choked with emotion. Cromwell, the physicist, said:

"We are your teachers and your fathers and your mothers, but we can't make this decision. You must tell us what to do. You know what to do. You know that, and you know that you must tell us."

Michael nodded, and then he told us what the children had decided. They had decided that the reservation must be maintained. They needed five more years. They decided that I was to go to Washington with Mark and with Dr.

Goldbaum—and somehow we were to get an extension of time. They felt that such an extension would not be too difficult to get at this point. Once we got the extension of time, they would be able to act.

"What kind of action?" Dr. Goldbaum asked them.

"There are too few of us," Michael said. "We need more. We must find new children, new infants, and we must bring them into the reservation. In other words, we must leave the reservation, some of us, and we must bring children here and we must educate the children here."

"But why must they be brought here?" Mark asked. "You can reach them wherever they are. You can go into their minds, you can make them a part of you. The children of the whole world are open to us. Why must you bring them here?"

"That may be true," Michael said, "but the crux of the matter is that the children can't reach us. Not for a long, long time. The children would be alone—and their minds would be shattered if we went into their minds. Tell us, what would the people of your world outside do to such children? What happened to people in the past who were possessed of devils, who heard voices, who heard the sound of angels? Some became saints, but many more were burned at the stake, destroyed, beaten to death, impaled, the victims of every horror that man could devise and inflict upon children."

"Can't you protect the children?" someone asked.

"Someday, yes. Now, no. There are simply not enough of us. First, we must help children to move here, hundreds and hundreds of children. Then we must create other reservations, other places like this one. It cannot be done quickly. It will take a long time. For a child, even our kind of child, to grow into an effective mover, it takes at least fifteen years. It is true that when we are eight, nine, ten years old, we know a great deal, we are able to do a great deal; but we are still children. That has not changed. So you see it will take a long, long time. The world is a very large place and there are a great many children. With all this, we must work carefully, very carefully. You see, people are afraid. Your lives, the lives of mankind, are ruled by fear. This will be the worst fear of all. They will go mad with fear, and all they will be able to think about is how to kill us. That will be their whole intention: to kill us, to destroy us."

"And our children could not fight back," Dr. Gold-baum said quietly. "That is something to remember, to think about; that is very important. You see, fighting, killing, hostility—this is the method of mankind. It has been the method of mankind for so long that we have never questioned it. Can a human being kill? Can a human being fight? We simply take it for granted that this is a human attribute. Take the case, for example, of the Israelis. For two thousand years the Jews had not, as a people, engaged in any kind of war, and it was said that they had lost the will to fight to kill; but you see that with the creation of Israel this will returned. So we say that there is no place on earth where man cannot learn very quickly to become a killer. When the people of India, who were such a people of peace, obtained their freedom from England, they turned upon each other in a fratricide unbelievable, unthinkable, monstrous. But our children are different. Our children cannot kill. This we must understand. No matter what danger faced them, no matter what fate they confronted, they could not kill. They cannot hurt a human being, much less kill one. The very act of hurt is impossible. Cattle, our old dogs and cats, they are one thing—but not people, not people."

(Here Dr. Goldbaum referred to the fact that we no longer slaughtered our cattle in the old way. We had pet dogs and cats, and when they became very old and sick, the children caused them peacefully to go to sleep—a sleep from which they never awakened. Then the children asked us if they might do the same with the cattle we butchered for food. But I must make one point specific, Harry, so that you will understand the children a little better: We butchered the cattle because some of us still required meat, but the children ate no meat. Almost from the very beginning, the children refused to eat meat. They ate eggs and vegetables, the fruit of the ground, but never meat. This eating of meat, the slaughtering of living things for eating, was a thing they tolerated in us with sadness. Discipline, you know, is also not a part of their being—that is, discipline in the sense that we understand it. They do not ask us not to do things. They will ask us positively to do something; but, on the other hand, if we do what to them is repulsive, no matter how obnoxious it may be to them, they will not ask us to stop doing it.)

"But not people," Dr. Goldbaum went on. "God help us, our children cannot hurt people. We are able to do things that we know are wrong. That remains one power we possess which the children lack. They cannot kill and they cannot hurt. Am I right, Michael, or is this only a presumption on my part?"

"Yes, you are right," Michael said. "We must do our work slowly and patiently, and the world must not know what we are doing until we have taken certain measures. We think we need three years more. We would like to have five years more. But, Jean, if you can get us three years, we will bear with that and somehow manage to do what we must do within that period. Now, will you go with Mark and with Dr. Goldbaum, and will you get us these three years, Jean?"

"Yes, I will get the three years," I said. "Somehow I will do what you need."

"And the rest of you," Michael said, "the rest of you are needed too. We need all of you to help us. Of course we will not keep any of you here if you wish to go. But, oh, we need you so desperately—as we have always needed you—and we love you and we cherish you, and we beg you to remain with us."

Do you wonder that we all remained, Harry, that no one of us could leave our children or will ever leave them now except when death takes us away? You see, Harry, they needed the time and they got the time, and that is why I can write this and that is why I can tell you so forthrightly what happened.

Mark and I and Dr. Goldbaum pleaded our case and we pleaded it well. We were given the years we needed, the additional years; and as for this gray barrier that surrounds us and the reservation, the children tell me that it is a simple device indeed. Of course that doesn't mean a great deal. They have a whole succession of devices that they call simple which are totally beyond the comprehension of any ordinary human being. But to come back to this barrier: as nearly as I can understand, they have altered the time sequence of the entire reservation; not by much—by less than one ten-thousandth of a second. But the result is that your world outside exists this tiny fraction of a second in the future. The same sun shines on us, the same winds blow, and from inside the barrier, we see your world unaltered. But you cannot see us. When you look at us, the present of our existence, the moment of time which we are conscious of at that moment of being in the universe, that moment has not yet come into existence; and instead of that, instead of reality, there is nothing: no space, no heat, no light, only the impenetrable wall of nonexistence. Of course you will read this, Harry, and you will say it makes absolutely no sense whatever, and I cannot pretend that I am able to make any sense out of it. I asked the children how to describe it. They told me as best they could, considering that they had to use the same words I use. They ask me to think of an existing area of time, of us traveling along this existing area with a point of consciousness to mark our progress. They have altered this point. And that means absolutely nothing to someone like myself.

I can only add this—from inside the reservation we are able to go outside, to go from the past into the future. After all, the crossover is only one ten-thousandth of a second. I myself have done this during the moments when we were experimenting with the barrier. I felt a shudder, a moment of intense nausea, but no more than that. There is also a way in which we return, but, understandably, I cannot spell that out.

So there is the situation, Harry. We will never see each other again, but I assure you that Mark and I are happier than we have ever been. Man will change; nothing in the world can halt that change. It has already begun. And in that change, man will become what he was intended to be, and he will reach out with love and knowledge and tenderness to all the universes of the firmament. I have written that down, Harry, and as I look upon it I find it the most thrilling idea I have ever encountered. My skin prickles at the mere thought. Harry, isn't this what man has always dreamed of? No war, no hatred, no hunger or sickness or death? How fortunate we are to be alive while this is happening! I think that we should ask no more.

So now I say goodbye to you, my dear brother, and I finish this letter.

With all my love,
Your sister, Jean Arbalaid.

Felton finished reading, and then there was a long, long silence while the two men looked at each other. Finally, the Secretary of Defense spoke, saying:

"You know, Felton, that we shall have to keep knocking at that barrier. We can't stop. We have to keep on trying to find the way to break through."

"I know."

"It will be easier, now that your sister has explained it."

"I don't think it will be easier," Felton said tiredly. "I don't think that she has explained it."

"Not to you and me, perhaps. But we'll put the egg-heads to work on it. They'll figure it out. They always do, you know."

"Perhaps not this time."

"Oh, yes," the Secretary of Defense nodded. "After all, Felton, we've got to stop it. We've had threats before, but not this kind of thing. I'm not going to dwell on the fact of this immorality, this godlessness, this nakedness, this depraved kind of sexual togetherness, this interloping into minds, this violation of every human privacy and every human decency. I don't have to dwell on that. You realize as well as I do, Felton, that this is a threat to every human being on the face of the earth. The kids were right. Oh, they understood this well enough, you know. This isn't a national threat; this isn't like Communism; this isn't simply a threat to the sovereignty, to the freedom of the United States, to the American way of life; this isn't just a threat to democracy; this is a threat to God Himself. This is a threat to mankind. This is a threat to everything decent, everything sacred, everything we believe in, everything we cherish. It's a disease, Felton. You know that, don't you? You recognize that—a disease."

"You really feel that, don't you?" Felton said. "You really believe what you are telling me."

"Believe it? Who can disbelieve it, Felton? It's a disease, and the only way to stop a disease is to kill the bugs that cause it. You know how you stop this disease? I'm going to say it and a lot more are going to say it, Felton: You kill the kids. It's the only way. I wish there were another way, but there isn't."

The End

ABOUT THE AUTHOR

HOWARD FAST was born in 1914 in New York City, where he lives today. Educated in the public schools, he published his first novel, *Two Valleys*, at the age of nineteen. Since then he has written twenty-three books, among them *Citizen Tom Paine*, *The Unvanquished*, *Freedom Road*, *Spartacus*, *April Morning*, and *Agrippa's Daughter*. Over twenty-five million copies of *Freedom Road* have been printed, and it is said to be the most widely read novel of this century.

Mr. Fast is married to the painter Bette Cohen and they have two children, Rachel, born 1944, and Jonathan, born 1948.